"I prefer to make my own decisions,"

Amber snapped. "I don't want them made for me."

Hamed was openly amused. "It's a pity you think the way you do. It will make my task twice as hard—persuading you that I am the right man to be your husband."

"I would say it's an impossible task," Amber persisted. "I'll fight you every inch of the way."

As she spoke, he pulled her into his arms. "You are reckoning without my expertise. In a few days you'll wonder why you ever resisted me."

"No doubt other women fall into your arms with absolutely no persuasion," Amber protested sarcastically.

"I must confess I don't usually have difficulty," admitted Hamed. "But the circumstances are different. You're the only woman I have ever wanted to marry. And make no mistake about it—you are going to be mine!"

Stormy Affair

by

MARGARET MAYO

Harlequin Books

TORONTO • LONDON • NEW YORK • AMSTERDAM
SYDNEY • HAMBURG • PARIS • STOCKHOLM

Original hardcover edition published in 1979
by Mills & Boon Limited

ISBN 0-373-02327-8

Harlequin edition published April 1980

Printed in U.S.A.

CHAPTER ONE

'PLEASE—pretty English lady—please come inside.'

For what seemed like the hundredth time Amber shrugged off the brown grasping hands that touched her bare shoulders and arms, scowling at the dark, always smiling faces which cajoled and beckoned her. She had been told that a visit to the souks was a must, but no one had warned her of the high-pressure salesmanship. Perhaps it was her long fair hair and creamy complexion that attracted them—a direct contrast to their own swarthy dark skins and shiny black hair—or was it the halternecked dress she wore? Whatever it was she felt that she was receiving more than her fair share of attention and began to wish that she had never wandered alone through the medina.

Amber had looked forward to this holiday in Tunisia, now it was turning into a nightmare. This excursion through the labyrinth of narrow streets with their frontless shops should have been a delight. Many examples of local craft were on display and to browse at leisure had been her aim—but the shopkeepers, it appeared, had different ideas. One particularly tenacious young man, with a disarming smile but a very firm grip, led her unwillingly inside—proudly pointing to his fine selection of leather pouffes and handbags, wallets and slippers.

'I'm sorry, I'm not interested in buying,' said Amber politely but firmly.

Her words, though, had little effect, for he kept her arm firmly grasped, pulling her close to him in an embarrassingly familiar manner. 'Here is a beautiful bag,' he said. 'Just five dinars, a special price because you are English.'

'I don't want it,' declared Amber, desperately trying to free herself. But the persistent young man pulled her from counter to counter pressing his goods upon her, never for one second letting go of her arm. Amber doubted whether she would get out of the shop without purchasing something and she felt the colour rising in her cheeks and perspiration breaking out on her forehead.

When a hand caught her other arm a rising panic threatened to choke her. Just what had she let herself in for? She closed her eyes, loth to see what was going to happen.

'*Sebhatemchi!*'

The voice was commanding and whatever he said it had the desired result, for the abashed young Tunisian released her at once. In relief Amber swung round, but her ready smile of thanks faded when she encountered the cool, dark eyes of her rescuer. His tall, broad frame dwarfed both herself and the shopkeeper. A blue silk shirt strained across powerful shoulders, immaculate trousers hugged muscular thighs. He looked out of place in the dusty medina with its countless souks and hundreds of Arabs—many old with gap-toothed smiles, others young and eager, but none dressed with the expensive elegance of this man.

Before she could speak Amber found herself ushered outside and through the busy jostling crowds, their pace not ceasing until they reached the main road.

The tall dark man then looked disparagingly down at Amber. 'If you couldn't cope you should have had more sense than to wander about alone—especially dressed like that. Tunisian men go for fair-skinned Europeans—did you not know that? What were you after—a cheap thrill?'

Looking about her at the Tunisian women with their white *sifsaris* which covered both their heads and their bodies, Amber did indeed feel under-dressed, at the same time realising why she herself had attracted attention, but she was determined not to let this auto-cratic stranger know this. 'It's warm and sunny,' she said tightly, 'I always dress like this on holiday.'

'It is all right on the beach, or in your hotel,' he said, 'but if you want my advice you will wear some-thing a little more modest next time you visit the souks—unless of course you enjoy being pawed!'

Amber's eyes, which were the same colour as her name, flashed angrily. 'How dare you speak to me like that. I don't need your advice and I don't know why you hauled me out of that shop as though I were in danger of my life. I'm quite capable of looking after myself.'

Thick brows rose to disappear in the thatch of dark hair which had fallen across his forehead. 'Really,' he mocked, 'you surprise me. I could have sworn there was a look of panic on your face.'

Amber shook her head crossly, her shoulder-length hair swinging about her face. Impatiently she brushed back a strand which caught across her cheek. 'You were imagining things. I was in perfect control of the situa-tion.'

'Then I do beg your pardon.' The dark head bowed

deferentially. 'My mistake. I was going to offer you a lift, but as you're so confident you can look after yourself I will take my leave.' He lifted his hand in salute. '*Filemáan.*'

Amber did not answer, merely glaring after his retreating back. Rude, arrogant, hateful—that was how she saw him. Interfering where he was not wanted. She could have coped; it was only a matter of being firm.

She crossed the road and made her way back towards the port and the bus stop. The streets of Sousse and the pavement cafés were crowded. All about her the male population of Tunisia were predominant. There were remarkably few women and the men, it seemed, had little else to do but stand and talk—except for the touts selling their cheap souvenirs.

Having just missed one bus and compelled to wait for the next Amber found herself surrounded by eager young pedlars anxious for a sale. One small boy who looked no more than ten told her that he would be whipped when he got home if he did not sell all of his baskets. How could she refuse? She had been told to barter, to offer at least half the asking price, but the boy stole her heart and willingly she handed over three dinars for a round basket that could be worth no more than one. Seeing this easy sale the other Arabs, hawking their silver necklaces or olive-wood bowls and statuettes, would not take no for an answer; standing uncomfortably close, their hands brushing her body in a way that she knew was no accident.

A loud horn distracted her attention and looking through the sea of faces before her Amber saw again the tall stranger, seated this time at the wheel of a sleek grey Mercedes. He beckoned her towards him, but Amber swung away haughtily. She needed no help—least of all from him.

'I do not wish to buy,' she repeated again and again, 'I'm not interested,' wishing fervently that the bus would hurry up. Out of the corner of her eye she saw that the Mercedes was still there and did not know which was the worst—the soliciting youths or the dark man watching, aware of her discomfort and waiting for her to turn to him for help.

'Okay,' she said at length, her nerves reaching breaking point. 'I'll buy a necklace and a bowl—then will you go?'

She had opened her purse when a hand reached out and took it from her. Her startled eyes encountered cool brown ones. 'I think you had better come with me,' he said, 'before you spend more than you can afford.'

About to refuse, Amber knew that he spoke sense. She did not really want these souvenirs, she could not afford to waste her money. Even so—she hesitated. But her mind was made up for her when he grabbed her wrist and pulled her unceremoniously forward and into his waiting car. The imperturbable Arabs followed, still flaunting their goods, their cheerful smiles very much in evidence.

When the car moved forward Amber could not help heaving a sigh of relief. Ungraciously she turned to the man at her side. 'I suppose I must thank you, though there was really no need, I'm——'

'I know,' he cut in blandly, 'you are quite capable of looking after yourself. But if that was an example I fear you must be harbouring a delusion. One needs to be firm. The slightest sign of weakness and you will never get rid of them.' His eyes flicked over the basket. 'I see you had already succumbed before I turned up. Did you really want that thing?'

'It's very nice,' she defended hotly. 'Besides, I felt sorry for the boy.'

'Precisely. They can all spin a good tale. They make their living out of gullible fools like you.'

Amber's lips tightened. So he thought her a fool, besides a cheap flirt. Well, she did not think much of him either—pushing in where he was not wanted. What was he trying to prove—and why the interest? Did he too have a hankering for fair-skinned Europeans, as he had put it, only his methods were far more subtle than his compatriots'? He spoke perfect English, though his looks denied that he was an Englishman. Dark-skinned, but not so dark as some of the locals, with unruly curling black hair, chiselled hawk-like features and a wide ruthless mouth. Good-looking, she admitted begrudgingly, wealthy too, judging by his fine clothes and expensive car, but it still puzzled her why he should choose to come to her rescue. 'I'm staying at the Sahara Beach,' she said coolly.

'Yes, I know,' came the surprising reply.

She wanted to ask how he knew, but aware that he expected this question she perversely remained silent. Perhaps he too was a holidaymaker there, though somehow she doubted it.

'I also know that you are holidaying alone,' he continued with annoying calm, 'so if I can be of any help in showing you the sights just say the word.'

What a nerve! Did he think she would allow a complete stranger in an alien country to take her out? He really must think her a fool. 'No, thanks. There are plenty of coach trips from the hotel. If I want to go anywhere I'll take one of them.'

'A pity. I would have enjoyed your company. You are a very attractive young lady.'

'Is that why you came to my—rescue—hoping I would agree to a date out of gratitude?'

The brows slid up smoothly. 'Not at all. I would have done the same for anyone.'

'So you make a habit of rescuing damsels in distress?'

His smile held little amusement. 'Only when they're as foolish as you. Not many English girls travel alone, whether it's because they have more sense or more friends I do not know. What made you do it?'

'I don't see that it's any business of yours.' Why should she tell him that she had no friends, that all the girls she had known had either drifted away or got married during the last two years when she had devotedly looked after her sick mother. She had not begrudged the time spent at home. She and her mother were very close, her father having been killed in a car accident when she was a baby. When two years ago it was discovered that her mother had a terminal illness she had given up her job to spend every minute at home. She had been heartbroken when her mother eventually died and very close to a breakdown herself. There had been a little money left after the funeral expenses and the doctor had urged her to take a holiday. Doctor Greer had been very kind, even going so far as to book the trip for her. It would be warm in Tunisia, he had said, and would do her good to get away from England's cold autumn days when the

first nip of frost was in the air. But all this was very
personal and she had no intention of discussing it with
a stranger.

He shrugged laconically. 'It's your prerogative. I
have no desire to force you into telling me something
you do not wish to.'

'I'm very glad to hear it,' said Amber primly, and
as they had now reached the end of the hotel drive
she gathered up her purchases. 'You can drop me
here.' But the barrier was lifted and they were through.
Apparently he had no intention of stopping until they
reached the hotel itself.

'Thank you for the lift,' she said, trying her hard-
est to be civil when all she really felt was intense antagonism towards this man who had against her wishes
played the part of the Good Samaritan.

He said, 'Next time you take a trip into town give
me a ring and I'll be more than pleased to be your
escort.' He thrust a card into her hand as she stepped
from the car and, unable to help herself, Amber stared
after him until the Mercedes disappeared from sight.
Only then did she walk slowly into the reception
lounge and up the stairs to her room.

It was not until she had washed and changed that
she looked at the card. Her first instinct had been to
tear it into little pieces, but curiosity got the better of
her and she picked it up, toying with it for a few
seconds before reading his name.

Hamed Ben Slouma, followed by an address and
telephone number—but no indication of what he did
for a living. Why did she feel disappointed? This man
meant nothing to her, so why the interest? She sat
down before the white-painted dressing table, placing

the card before her and staring at her reflection in the mirror. Clear wide-set eyes, a short turned-up nose, nicely shaped lips, golden hair that flicked back naturally. There was nothing special about her—nothing that warranted this man's attention, so why had he chosen to single her out? The fact that he knew she had travelled alone *and* which hotel she was staying in proved that he had known of her existence before today. She shivered despite the heat. It was unnerving, to say the least. Perhaps there had been some ulterior motive behind his assistance? With fingers that trembled she picked up the card and tore it into tiny pieces, flinging them savagely into the waste paper basket.

She picked up her bag and let herself out of the room. It was time for lunch. There was a determined air about her as she walked along the corridor, a forced smile on her lips. From now on she would push the handsome Tunisian from her mind. It was highly unlikely that they would meet again and she certainly had no intention of getting in touch.

Amber spent the afternoon by the swimming pool, lying on one of the wooden-mattressed sun-loungers provided by the hotel. It was an idyllic life and up until today she had enjoyed it to the full. Already, after only a few days, she had felt a lessening of the tension inside her, the fatigue that her mother's long illness had induced was beginning to fade. With the resilience of youth she had begun to spring back to life and had looked forward eagerly to each new day.

Her meeting with Hamed Ben Slouma had spoilt this happiness. She was not sure why. He had come to her help; he was charming, incredibly handsome, and had done nothing against which she could take offence, yet somehow a shadow had crossed her path. Annoyed with herself now for allowing her thoughts to return to the stranger, Amber struggled to her feet and dived cleanly into the pool. Despite the warmth of the sun the water was icy cold and took her breath away, but she determinedly swam several lengths. The exercise helped drive away these unbidden thoughts.

The Sahara Beach was a large hotel with three seven-storey blocks each joined by a wide corridor, but despite its size the atmosphere was friendly and Amber had already made several friends. She shared her dining table with a young married couple, Elsa and David Flemming, and a French girl, Nicolette, who had also come to Tunisia alone.

Over dinner that evening Nicolette asked Amber how she had enjoyed her day in Sousse. It should have been the most natural thing in the world to tell her about the stranger who had virtually plucked her from the medina, but for some reason she kept this news to herself, enthusing instead about the souks abounding with people and the variety of goods on display. 'There's absolutely everything,' she said, 'leatherwork, Arabian pointed slippers, gold and silver jewellery, sheepskin rugs—oh, all sorts of things. I didn't have time to see it all. It's an experience you mustn't miss.'

'We were thinking of going ourselves tomorrow,' said Elsa. 'If you want to join us, you're welcome.'

But Amber shook her head, memories of this morning all too raw for her to consider venturing into Sousse again. She had no desire to bump into *that* man.

'I might go before the end of the holiday,' she said, 'but I'm going to spend a lazy day on the beach tomorrow,' adding lightheartedly, 'I can't go back without a sun-tan!'

Nicolette said, 'I'll join you, Amber. I am definitely a lazy person. My idea of a holiday is to spend all my time in the sun.'

Amber knew that Nicolette, like herself, had come to Tunisia as a sort of pick-me-up after a recent illness, but up until now she had kept herself very much to herself, even though Amber had suggested several times doing something together. Now she said, 'That will be lovely,' glad of the opportunity of company, since it would help keep her mind off certain things that she would prefer to forget.

After dinner, as had become their practice, they all went into the lounge for coffee and drinks. Normally they remained there until it was time to go to bed. There was a resident band and a small square for dancing. It was all very pleasant and Amber had never been short of partners, although she had never encouraged anyone. She had no intention of becoming involved in a holiday romance. This holiday was supposed to help her get over the heartache of her mother's death, not involve herself in more.

Up until now she had succeeded, but tonight she found it impossible to relax, and when shortly after nine Nicolette announced she was going to have an early night Amber decided to join her. She would read a book—the one thing guaranteed to help her sleep—otherwise she could see herself lying awake half the night.

Nicolette's room was in a different block and they

chatted for a few moments outside the lounge before going their separate ways. For once Amber decided to use the lift—normally she walked up the two flights of stairs, telling herself it was good exercise—but tonight she felt lazy.

Her finger was on the button when an unmistakable voice called, 'Miss Christy!' A prickling sensation ran down her spine and deciding to pretend she had not heard Amber remained facing the lift doors, willing it to come quickly so that she could scoot in before he reached her.

Again he called her and this time she had no option but to turn. He was closer than she expected and surprised she stepped back, vividly aware of the curious sardonic smile, the cool appraisal of those enigmatic brown eyes. His light suit enhanced the darkness of his skin, emphasised his breadth of shoulder.

'Mr—er—Slouma! I didn't expect to see you again.'

'You are afraid of me.' It was a statement rather than a question. 'There is no need. I mean you no harm.'

Amber wore a long white dress of a clinging silky material with shoestring straps and a revealing neckline. Her hands fluttered nervously to her throat. This man seemed unable to take away his eyes and she felt as though he was mentally undressing her. 'Perhaps you don't,' she said, her voice lacking conviction, 'but I know nothing about you. So far as I'm concerned you're a complete stranger, and I object to strangers looking at me as you are now.'

He shrugged expressively. 'I am a man—and you have a very beautiful body. Why should I not admire it? Besides, everyone is a stranger at some time in their life. Join me for a drink and we will remedy the situation.'

At that precise moment the lift came. Amber had never felt more thankful for anything in her life. She stepped smartly inside. 'I'm sorry, Mr Slouma, but I'm tired. Goodnight.' She smiled, a tight smile that was an effort, and pressed the button for her floor. It was not until she had tried several times without success that she realised he was holding the button outside which kept the doors open.

'I said I would like you to join me.' And the way he said it and the way he looked at her told Amber that it would be advisable to agree. Otherwise she would not put it past him to step into the lift and accompany her to her room.

'Very well.' With resigned reluctance she moved towards him. He was much taller than she and at close quarters a distinct musky smell emanated from him. Clean-shaven, smart, handsome—why did she not like him? What was there about him that made her wary? Had she met him in England his masculine virility, the foreign good looks, would have attracted her immediately. There was something about him that would fascinate most women—but here where life was so totally different she felt nothing but apprehension.

His smile was charged with triumph and the hand on her elbow as he ushered her back towards the lounge slightly proprietorial. Amber wanted to pull away, but Hamed Ben Slouma was as yet an unknown quantity and she deemed it wise not to do so. Already she had seen the masterful side of his nature, making her aware that he was a man who knew what he wanted and always won. She imagined him to be utterly ruthless—the determined chin and cool dark eyes told her that—and anyone who defied him would soon wish they hadn't.

The lounge was now crowded, but they managed to find two empty seats in a corner. He signalled the waiter and without asking what she would like ordered a Martini, and a whisky for himself. It was her favourite drink, but how had he known? There was so much he knew about her. Had she been secretly observed for the last few days? There was no other explanation, but the thought caused a chill to creep through her veins and it was all she could do to control a shiver.

'Now tell me why you were going to bed at such an early hour,' he said, his arm resting nonchalantly across the back of her seat. 'It is not your normal practice.'

'And how would you know what I normally do?' flashed Amber. The lights in the room were low and it was difficult to read correctly the expression on his face. His tone, though, suggested he was mocking and a flame of irritation shot through her, making her voice sharper than usual.

'I know a great deal about you,' he said, his voice softly sensuous, like a caress. 'I know, for instance, that this holiday is to help you get over a recent bereavement.'

'What are you?' asked Amber defensively, 'a private detective? Is it your rule to find out about girls before you make a date with them?'

Unperturbed by her angry outburst, he said, 'Only the very special ones.'

'And in what way am I special?' Amber's heart pumped erratically, her fingers clenching her bag.

'That would be telling.' A secretive smile played on

his lips. 'A little mystery adds zest to life, do you not agree?'

Out of the corner of her eye Amber saw that Elsa and David had observed her reappearance with the handsome Arab. It would be difficult trying to explain him away tomorrow. She edged away from the disturbing nearness of his arm, uneasily aware of the effect he had on her. 'Not when it means I've been spied on,' she returned hotly. 'You have no right, and I demand that you leave me alone!'

Fractionally his eyes narrowed. 'I do not think you can say that I have disturbed you in any way. In fact before this morning you were unaware of my presence.'

'But since your—unwelcome rescue—you feel you can stake a claim on my company. Is that it?' and on a higher note, as she suddenly realised exactly what had happened, 'I *knew* I was in no real danger. It was all an act—your way of getting to know me. You're as bad as the rest of them!' Amber was visibly shaking now and would have risen had her companion not laid a detaining hand on her arm.

'Calm down, Amber, or your friends over there will think I am trying to molest you.'

But she was past caring what anyone thought. 'It's *Miss Christy* to you,' she snapped, 'and my friends wouldn't be far wrong.' The waiter brought their drinks, but Amber ignored them and said, 'I'm going to my room now and if you stop me I shall call the management. Oh, and please don't try to see me again, Mr Slouma, because I shan't be available.'

Head erect, she rose from her seat and stiffly wove her way through the couples on the dance floor. There had been a murmur of interest around them and she felt several pairs of eyes following her. Damn Hamed Ben Slouma, she thought expressively, trying not to let it show that she was in any way upset.

The stairs were only a few yards away from the lounge entrance and she had her foot on the first step when a hand on her arm swung her about. Face to face yet again with the person she had sought to escape, she opened her mouth, intending to call out to the man behind the reception desk, but hard ruthless lips suddenly descended on hers, effectively stemming her protest.

Amber could not deny the leaping response his savage kiss drew from her and the fire that coursed through her veins shook her so much that her lips trembled when he let her go. She could do nothing but look up at him, her golden eyes wide with mute appeal.

He laughed harshly, triumphantly, 'Goodnight, *habibati*, pleasant dreams,' and he walked out of the hotel.

CHAPTER TWO

FOR several long seconds Amber stood motionless and then with actions that were purely automatic she slowly mounted the stairs. It was not until she was safely inside her room that anger took over. Why, she asked herself, had she allowed Hamed Ben Slouma to kiss her? Why had she not struggled, screamed for help? It appalled her to think how meekly she had accepted his caress, and what was more disgusting was her own unexpected repsonse. No wonder he had laughed! His expertise was unquestionable. Did all women respond as she had? Did he enjoy flaunting his ability to attract the opposite sex?

She felt sickened and in a fit of self-loathing went into the bathroom and washed her face, scrubbing at her lips with her washcloth until she was sure all traces of his kiss had been erased. If he turned up again tomorrow she really would complain to the management. Men like him needed putting behind bars!

Nor surprisingly Amber found it difficult to sleep. Each time she closed her eyes a handsome dark face with black curly hair and laughing brown eyes taunted her. Even when she tried to read his face became super-imposed across the printed page, and in despair she flung the book across the room. Had she been at home she could have gone downstairs and heated herself a glass of milk, but here in the hotel there was nothing she could do. Eventually, though, mental and physical exhaustion got the better of her and for several hours Hamed Ben Slouma was shut out from her mind.

When morning came she was able to laugh at the events of last night, telling herself that she had over-reacted. Hamed Ben Slouma was no different from the other men he had warned her about. A firm hand was all she needed. If he had the nerve to turn up today she would tell him politely to go away, and that would be that.

She was glad Elsa and David were absent from the breakfast table. It meant that for a while at least no awkward questions would be asked. She cut through her roll, spreading it liberally with butter, concentrating intently on her task, determined to push Hamed from her mind—an idea instantly doomed when Nicolette joined her, saying, 'What happened to you last night? I thought you were going to bed early.'

'I changed my mind, but how did you know?' replied Amber cautiously, although it was not difficult to guess that she had bumped into the Flemmings who would lose no time in telling her all about Amber's new Arab friend.

Nicolette smiled knowingly. 'I hear you were with a handsome man. How did you meet him?'

Amber shrugged, pretending indifference. 'In Sousse yesterday, didn't I tell you? He's no one in particular. Are you still going down to the beach this morning?'

Nicolette, however, had no intention of changing the subject. 'Elsa said he looked affluent. Aren't you lucky meeting someone rich—and handsome. Are you seeing him again?'

'I hope not,' returned Amber strongly. 'I told him last night to keep out of my way.'

'Elsa said it looked as though you were arguing,' persisted the French girl, 'but I couldn't believe that, not on such a short acquaintance—unless he was trying to——' She broke off, looking slightly embarrassed.

Amber laughed mirthlessly. 'He was making a nuisance of himself, but not in the way you think. I'd really rather not talk about him, if you don't mind.'

Clearly Nicolette did mind, but she asked no further questions and the two girls spent a lazy morning on the beach, saying little, content to soak up the sun. Amber tried to steer her thoughts away from Hamed, but they returned with unerring accuracy. Exactly why was he interested in her? And if she had been discreetly observed for days why had he waited until now before making himself known?

Several times Nicolette looked at her curiously and Amber knew she was hardly being fair. Had the positions been reversed she herself would have wanted to ask questions, but nevertheless she chose to retain her silence. If Hamed took her at her word she would not see him again, so what point was there in discussing him?

They lunched and in the afternoon swam lazily in one of the outside pools. The weather remained fine—blue skies, sunshine, pleasant company, what more could anyone desire? Yet for all that Amber found it impossible to relax completely. All the time she was aware that Hamed might turn up—even now he could be watching her. It made her wary and constantly she scanned the figures scattered about the pool.

By four o'clock the sun began to sink. People gathered up their belongings and returned inside and Nicolette and Amber followed suit. There were still three hours before dinner, but Nicolette declared she

was going to spend them in her room and Amber somewhat reluctantly thought it might be as well to do
the same.

Then she thought, why should I? Why should I let
this man ruin my holiday? So she showered and changed
into a pair of white jeans and a bright green knitted
top. Downstairs in the lounge she ordered tea, looking
about her as she sipped it, realising with something
approaching sadness that she was the only one to sit
alone. Until now it had not bothered her, she had
been full of grief over her mother's death and had lived
in a world of her own, little caring what went on outside it. Now, though, she had become alive again and
felt conspicuous. She looked for a friendly face but saw
only open curiosity and an occasional whisper, heads
nodding in her direction. The events of last night were
being discussed, at her expense. What did she do—sit
here and pretend to ignore them, or get up and go?
The latter was a coward's way out, but one which she
was tempted to take. She finished her tea and stood up
and then for some unknown reason her eyes were drawn
across the room. Hamed Ben Slouma's dark eyes were
upon her. She tripped and would have fallen had not
a helping hand caught her arm. 'Thank you,' she smiled
automatically at the gentleman who had saved her.

'It might be as well if you look where you are going,'
he said kindly. 'Your admirer might be put off by a
black eye or a broken arm.'

The words were meant well and had been spoken
lightheartedly, but Amber, annoyed that he should
have seen the reason why she tripped, said hotly, 'I'll
thank you to mind your own business!'

Immediately the words were out she regretted them,

but it was too late to do anything about it. She moved swiftly out of the lounge, running up the stairs to her room, her whole body aflame with embarrassment. Once inside she sat down on the edge of the bed, breathing deeply, aware of a white-hot anger burning inside. She was angry with Hamed Ben Slouma for no other reason than his being there and angry with herself for being foolish. He had made no attempt to seek her out—maybe he had taken notice of her request—but even so his very presence was disturbing. Her heartbeats had quickened alarmingly and she would have liked to tell herself that it was fear. But was it? She had a sneaking suspicion that they meant more than that—that it was the man himself who did this to her. With surprising clarity she realised that it was only since meeting him that she had thought less about her own grief—he had become the number one thought in her mind. Why? Was it simply because he had shown an interest in her, or could it be that her own interest in Hamed Ben Slouma went deeper than she thought? He was undeniably attractive, and for him to single her out—well, any girl would be flattered.

'I'm behaving like a schoolgirl,' she thought in horror, 'instead of a young lady of nineteen.' But there had been no one before him, there had not been time, so she felt she could be forgiven for feeling as she did now. But, she told herself firmly, she could not allow this state of affairs to go on. She must pull herself together and not let Hamed Ben Slouma see that he in any way affected her.

She was presuming he would still be there that evening and if she failed to turn up he would know that she was purposely avoiding him. The best thing to do—if he approached her—was to treat him with polite indifference, maintain a calmness she knew she would be far from feeling, but if she could keep this fact from him then she would have achieved what she set out to do.

Nicolette and Elsa and David were already at the table when Amber eventually entered the dining room half an hour later than usual. She had reluctantly gone down knowing they would bring up the subject of her dark admirer, and was pleasantly surprised when throughout the meal no mention was made of him.

Instead Elsa and David regaled them with a full description of their day in Sousse. They had enjoyed it enormously and had come back armed with all sorts of gifts. 'You should have heard David bartering,' laughed Elsa. 'He had it down to a fine art before he'd finished. He must have saved us pounds!'

'Remind me to take him with me next time,' joked Amber. 'I'm afraid I'm too soft.'

'We must all go,' suggested David. 'I believe if several of us buy a similar thing then we get it even cheaper.'

They all laughed. Thrift was obviously one of David's strong points.

In the lounge later Elsa said, 'There's a cabaret on in the Night Club tonight. Anyone fancy going?'

'You can count me out,' said Nicolette immediately. 'It does not start until nine. I shall never get up in the morning.'

Nicolette's early nights were becoming something of a joke and David said, 'I think you must have some-one hidden in your room, you spend so much time there. Aren't you going to let us into your secret?'

The French girl laughed goodnaturedly. 'It is Amber who has the secrets, not me. Why don't you ask her about her secret admirer?' adding mischievously, 'I expect he would like to go to her room.'

'Nicolette!' exclaimed Amber in horror. 'There's nothing like that. Why, I don't even like the man. He's a bore, pushing his nose in where he's not wanted. If he turns up tonight I'm jolly well going to put him in his place!'

'That should be quite interesting.'

Amber watched in horror as her companions raised their eyes above her head in the direction of the voice. She herself looked round more slowly at the man who was fast becoming less of a stranger. His words had belied his real feelings. Interest was the last thing she read there. Cold disapproval was predominant, followed closely by tightly checked anger. His eyes were darker than she remembered seeing them; like black ice, she thought, and shivered.

'Eavesdroppers never hear good of themselves,' she challenged, 'and besides, I only spoke the truth.'

'Then I should like to hear some more truths.' He looked at the three people seated round the table, their mouths agape, watching this byplay with interest. 'If you will excuse, Miss Christy, I feel this is something we should discuss in private.'

Nicolette was the first to recover. 'But of course. Lovers' tiffs are always best settled—alone.' She looked up at Hamed Ben Slouma with something approaching reverence.

Amber felt disgusted. No doubt this was the effect he had on most women. How fortunate that she could claim to be a little different, but wait until she got Nicolette alone! Lovers' tiff indeed! Hamed Ben Slouma and she were not even friends, yet alone lovers. The fact that she went hot at the thought of such an association was something that she preferred not to dwell on. 'I'm not sure that I want to be alone with you,' she said. 'Can't it be dealt with here and now?'

His lips tightened. 'I have no desire to air our differences in public.'

'But these are my friends,' insisted Amber. Suddenly she did not want to be alone with this man. His nearness disturbed her. Even now his presence caused a tingling sensation through her veins, as though some magnetic impulse attracted her to him. How could she retain that cool she had planned, feeling this way? 'Whatever has to be said can be said in front of them.'

'I think not.' Again that masterful attitude. He moved to her side and put his hand beneath her elbow, giving her little choice but to go with him.

She cast a pleading glance at her companions, but they, it appeared, had eyes only for Hamed Ben Slouma and were totally oblivious to Amber's anguish. She could almost read their minds. 'What a handsome man,' they were thinking. 'What a fool Amber must be to spurn his advances.' Especially Nicolette. It was the first time she had seen him, but it was not difficult to imagine which way her thoughts ran. She could have him willingly, thought Amber, if he would only leave her alone.

He led her to a table at the other end of the room. Defiantly she sat opposite rather than at his side, not missing the sudden tautening of his expression as she did so. She sat back, trying to appear relaxed—difficult when inside she was curled as tightly as a spring. In contrast Hamed Ben Slouma sat on the edge of his seat, legs apart, elbows resting lightly on his knees, his hands linked together. She found herself looking at his hands. They were well shaped with long lean fingers; strong hands that could either caress—or inflict pain. Now why should she think that? she asked herself. He had never hurt her. Yet somehow she knew. A man as ruthless as he would not be adverse to meting out punishment if he thought fit.

'So I am a bore,' he said in a low controlled voice. 'Do you consider you know me well enough to judge my character?'

Amber lifted her eyes to his face. He was studying her intently, as if trying by his very thoroughness to read her mind. 'I know you as well as I'm ever likely to—and in that respect, yes, I do consider you a bore. Any man who pushes in where he's not wanted I would place in the same category.'

'Do you categorise all men?'

Only the ones I don't like, Amber felt like saying, but that would have been a lie. Neither did she want to tell him that she had met remarkably few men in her life—and especially no one like him. His whole attitude, his bearing, was completely different. He was a cut above other men, she admitted grudgingly. Completely self-assured, never failing to get what he wanted. A man who had made his mark in life. Again she wondered what he did for a living that could allow him so much free time. 'Not particularly,' she shrugged, 'it's just that you—you——'

She hesitated and he finished for her, 'Made quite

an impression? I had hoped it was a good one, but it appears I am mistaken.'

Amber's eyes widened. 'How can it matter what I feel? Am I supposed to be eternally in your debt?' He really was expecting too much! 'Just tell me what it is you want and let's get it over with.'

'A little of your time.' His eyes never left her face, seeking her reaction.

Amber could think of only one reason why he should desire her company. 'Do you mean you want an affair?' Why else should he make this strange request? And why had he singled her out in the first place? The fact that he knew so much about her filled her with misgivings.

The idea seemed to amuse him. 'It wasn't exactly what I had in mind, but if that's what you're offering?'

Amber knew it would be wise to ignore his mockery, but the taunting smile and those unfathomable dark eyes incensed her and she flashed back, 'You know very well that that's not what I meant. Just who are you, Mr Slouma?'

'I am your friend,' he replied, as if the question had never been in doubt. 'I sense you are a little afraid—afraid perhaps of the unknown. You do not give yourself a chance.'

'I'm not accustomed to being—picked up by strange men,' she returned haughtily.

He shook his head in annoyance. You persist in calling me a stranger. Haven't you got to know me—just a little?'

'Oh yes. I know for instance that you're a very persistent man. You must also be either very lazy or very rich, otherwise you wouldn't be able to spend so much time spying on me.'

It was gratifying to see the effect her words had. His lips tightened and his fingers curled into fists, but he held his temper in check admirably, for when he spoke his voice was perfectly controlled. 'An unfortunate word, perhaps, when I have only your best interests at heart.'

'But why me?' persisted Amber. 'Tell me that—is it too much to ask? Can't you see that it's the uncertainty that's off-putting? How do I know your motives are honourable? For all I know you could be planning to murder me!'

He looked thoughtful for a moment. 'Perhaps you are right, but even so I do not feel at liberty to disclose my reasons. I can assure you, though, that I mean you no harm.'

He sounded sincere. Amber was almost inclined to believe him, but certain niggling doubts still remained. Her brow was creased as she answered, 'I don't feel like taking that chance.'

'Then it will be up to me to persuade you. Come, let us dance.'

Amber had not even noticed that the band had begun playing or that the lounge had filled. This evening she had chosen to wear a dress that fastened high at the neck and when Hamed's hand slid round her back she was glad of the thin material that protected her skin from his touch. The tune was slow and dreamy. Hamed was an expert dancer and although Amber had never had very much time for dancing she had no difficulty in following him. He held her close, his thighs touching hers, his warm breath fanning her hair. But even so there was nothing suggestive about his embrace. His natural rhythm indicated his love of music, and moving in unison with his steps Amber felt herself relax.

Out of the corner of her eye she saw her friends' heads turned in their direction, although the subdued lighting made it difficult to read their expressions. She guessed they would register approval. How embarrassing it was to have one's affairs watched over so closely—and no doubt they read more into it than there actually was. She had been given no choice when he suggested they dance—no matter what the others might think. There was no softening on her part. She still had no intention of becoming too friendly with this persistent stranger.

But despite her antagonism Amber could not help enjoying dancing with him. Their bodies moved as one and the pressure of his hand on her back increased fractionally. 'It is good,' he said, 'you are now relaxed. Perhaps we shall fight no more?'

Amber allowed him a weak smile. 'Perhaps.'

The rhythm changed. Popular beat music took its place and Hamed indicated that they leave the floor. Back in their seats Amber saw Nicolette and the other couple leave the room. 'I must go,' she said, grasping the excuse. 'We've arranged to go to the Night Club.'

One brow lifted sardonically. 'It looks to me as though your friends are going without you. I expect they think you would rather be with me.'

He sounded smug and Amber sprang to her own defence. 'I doubt it. They know exactly how I feel about you.'

'Oh yes, I remember, you were telling them when I so rudely interrupted. But they've gone now, so you will have to put up with my company after all.'

'There's nothing to stop me joining them.'

'Only me.' His eyes held hers, daring her to defy him, and Amber knew that there was little to be gained by so doing. He had followed her last night, he would again. She would be creating a scene for nothing. He was not a man to treat lightly, that much she had learned. But even so she could not help saying:

'Of course, I'd almost forgotten, you think only of yourself.' She spoke sarcastically; unusual for her, but then this was an unusual experience. 'It doesn't matter what I want to do.'

'On the contrary,' he said smoothly, 'I have every desire to make you happy.'

'But only when it pleases you?'

He shrugged lazily. 'Is that a bad thing? I am sure you will find me very good company. Try me to-morrow. I will take you into Tunis and show you our very fine capital.'

Amber had no intention of going anywhere with Hamed, but to say no now would mean the entire evening would be spent arguing. So she said, 'I'll see. I'll let you know later.'

He looked pleased as though sure that her ultimate answer would be yes. It would be interesting to see his reaction when he found out she had no intention of going. A subconscious smile played on her lips. She could almost look forward to it. Hamed Ben Slouma did not strike her as a man used to having his offers of friendship spurned—it could do him good. She sipped the Martini he had ordered, twisting in her seat to watch the dancers.

The next moment she felt Hamed beside her, his shoulder brushing hers. She turned her head to look into the mirror-hard surface of his eyes. 'When I'm with a girl I like to receive her full attention,' he said coldly, 'not look at the back of her head.'

Amber inched away. 'I think I can safely say that things are somewhat different as far as we're concerned. Ours is not the normal man-woman relationship. I don't feel I owe you anything.'

'Of course you don't *owe* me anything,' he said impatiently, 'all I'm asking is a little common courtesy. Why must you be so difficult?'

'Am I?' asked Amber with assumed innocence. 'Perhaps it's because I hate being pestered. I didn't come here to find myself a boy-friend. I came for a rest. If you know so much about me you'll know that for the last two years I've nursed my sick mother. I feel utterly exhausted, and your persistence in trying to claim my friendship is wearing me down still further.'

He looked at her for several long moments after she had finished talking, an unfathomable expression in those deep dark eyes, then he lifted his hand and stroked her cheek gently. 'Poor Amber, alone in the big cruel world, fighting off the hand of friendship that could help her through these dark days.'

The irony in his voice annoyed her and she knocked away his arm, her eyes flashing. 'I'll say one thing for you, Mr Slouma, you're very persistent, but it's not going to get you anywhere. If you want to pick yourself up a girl you'd better try your luck with someone else. My friend Nicolette, for instance. Judging by the way she looked at you earlier you should have no difficulty in that direction.'

'The French girl? She's attractive, certainly, but I prefer to choose my own friends.'

'Despite the fact that they might not want your friendship?' Amber countered hotly. 'Don't you ever stop to think of other people's feelings?' The more time she spent in the company of this man the more irate she became. Why could he not see that he was being a nuisance? It really was incredible the way he kept pushing himself. Was he so thick-skinned that he was unaware of her attitude, or was it pride that would not let him admit that here was one girl who did not fall immediately at his feet?

'I don't think it's a matter of me considering your feelings,' he said coolly, 'more you considering your own. Do you prefer to spend your days alone? Wouldn't you find life much more enjoyable with an attentive man at your side?'

Amber looked at him obliquely. 'I might. It would depend on the man. You don't know me very well or you'd know that I'm not the type of girl to allow myself to be picked up.'

He smiled bitterly. 'You mean had I been introduced to you formally it would make all the difference?'

She did not mean that, and he knew it. He was deliberately trying to trick her into something she would regret later. 'You know very well what I mean,' she said savagely. 'This conversation is getting us nowhere.' She picked up her drink and took a mouthful of the pale liquid, almost choking in her eagerness to appear undisturbed. He really was the most exasperating man she had ever met!

'Then we shall talk about something else,' he said smoothly. 'Tell me about yourself—about your childhood. Have you any brothers or sisters?'

But Amber was in no mood for pleasantries. 'Why should I discuss my personal life with you? If you really want to know I'm sure you're devious enough to find out for yourself.'

His lips firmed and the cool dark eyes glittered. As he leaned towards her Amber saw a pulse beating high in his jaw, noticed for the first time that there were lighter coloured flecks in his eyes and a barely discernible hint of grey at his temples. 'You are pushing me too far,' he said grimly. 'I am not used to being spoken to like this.' He caught her wrist between his fingers, gripping it so tightly that Amber felt certain it would break. 'I have done nothing to deserve your—contempt. I have gone out of my way to help you, to try and make your life more pleasant—and I *demand* some sort of response.'

'You mean I have to pay for the price of your friendship—a friendship I never wanted in the first place?' Amber hissed, her eyes narrowed, her face only inches away from his.

His fingers tightened and it was all she could do to stop herself crying out with pain. 'I mean I want your company and until you agree to come out with me I shall not leave you alone.'

He meant every word, but she was not going to let him blackmail her so easily. 'You talk big, Mr Hamed Ben Slouma, but let me tell you this, no man has ever dictated to me before and I'm quite sure you're not going to do so now. Maybe you thought I looked helpless that day you saw me in the medina, but I'm not.

I'm strong and I have a mind of my own, and if I don't want to do something no one will make me!'

For a brief space something sparked in his eyes, a touch of humour maybe, but it was gone instantly, leaving Amber to believe she had imagined it. 'It is good you have spirit,' he said. 'I despise weak women.' The pressure of his fingers eased slightly but still he did not release her, instead he pulled her closer towards him. 'I think that before long you will change your mind.' His breath was warm on her cheek. 'I have methods of persuasion that are rarely known to fail.'

Alarm flickered inside Amber, the rapid beating of her heart painful against her breast. Eyes widened with appeal, she looked into the velvet brown depths of his. They held her gaze steadily until she felt mesmerised, unable to turn one way or the other. Even when his fingers cupped her chin she remained immobile, heedless of those around her, conscious only of the dark, handsome face which blocked out everything else from her line of vision.

With infinite slowness his face drew nearer and although she knew he was going to kiss her she was powerless to move. When his mouth closed on hers she was utterly unprepared for the onslaught of her senses. She should have remembered, recalled the one other occasion when his lips had taken hers and opened up a whole new tide of emotions she had hitherto been unaware of. This was no gentle kiss, but sensual and savage, demanding a response. Her lips parted of their own volition. It was as though they did not belong to her, as though an alien being had taken over and was responding to Hamed in the manner that he desired.

Her fingers curled round his neck and she pulled his dark head close.

When he pushed her from him there was victory lighting those dark eyes. 'And now, my little passion flower, what is to be your answer now?'

CHAPTER THREE

ONCE free from Hamed's embrace Amber felt consumed by a burning shame. How easily she had given herself. How exultant he felt! Her eyes fell before his and had it been possible she would have fled the room, but after having caused a minor sensation last night she did not intend a repeat performance. 'You're a swine,' she said softly but vehemently.

His mouth quirked. 'I did not notice you resisting. I thought—no, I hoped, you had come to your senses. Was I wrong?'

'Completely,' she said with conviction. 'I didn't want to cause a scene, that's all. Your kisses don't mean that much to me,' and she flicked her fingers in contempt.

'I think you are trying to convince yourself, not me. Come——' he stood up abruptly, 'it is time we danced again.'

On the floor he held her close, his hand on her back moving with sensuous expertise, her body pressed against the hard lean strength of his. Last night he had said he wanted only her company; now it appeared he was looking for something more. She deliberately resisted him even though his nearness set her pulses racing. She could not understand why a man she despised should have this effect on her. Was it her surroundings that made her so weak—the heady exotic flavour of this North African country, or the idle life she was now spending in utter contrast to her previous stren-

uous existence when there were never enough hours
in the day? Had it upset her equilibrium to such an
extent that she had practically given herself to the
first man who came along? Her cheeks flamed and she
rested her head on his shoulder so that he should not
see.

His other hand came up to stroke her hair and
Amber felt a sudden ridiculous urge to fling her arms
about his neck. Instead she tried to push him away. At
close quarters like this she was defenceless—and he
knew it—and the thought was agonising. She felt
cheapened, immoral almost. It did not seem right that
she should enjoy being in the arms of this foreigner—
this tall, devastatingly handsome man who was beginning to take over her life.

When he said, 'Amber, will you come to Tunis with
me tomorrow?' she found herself agreeing. Again it
was that other alien being who had taken over. It was
not the Amber she knew who had acquiesced so easily.
That could never be.

For the rest of the evening they danced and drank,
talking little, Hamed now quietly content, Amber
somewhat apprehensive, wondering exactly what she
had let herself in for.

When at half past ten he suggested she might like
to go to bed because of the necessity for an early start
the next morning, she agreed readily. Outside the
lounge doors they parted company; he did not kiss her
again, he did not even touch her. She should have been
grateful; instead she felt disappointed.

He had not said what time he would meet her, but
when Amber came out of the dining room the next

morning, having breakfasted early, he was waiting. Still more than a little ashamed about her reaction to his kiss, Amber greeted him coolly. He was not perturbed, almost as though he did not notice she was anything other than pleased to see him. 'I'm glad you're ready,' he said. 'I had visions of coming up to your room to fetch you.'

'I said I would come,' she said in a tight little voice. 'I never go back on my word.'

'I must remember that,' he replied gravely.

His sleek grey Mercedes was low and comfortable, but Amber herself felt far from easy. She had lain awake for most of the night worrying about today. She knew so little about Hamed. How did she know he could be trusted?

Almost as though he guessed something of her inner torment he said, 'Relax, Amber. You have no need to fear me. You are perfectly safe.'

She looked at him scornfully. 'You flatter yourself! Why should I feel afraid? I wouldn't be here if I were.'

'Little liar. You are as easy to read as a book. But I don't want you to feel this way. I want you to be happy and relaxed in my company.'

If only that were possible, but Hamed was a stranger, an unknown quantity, how could she feel secure? In England it would have been different, but here in this strange place with its totally different way of life she felt afraid. This man had pursued her for reasons known only to himself. How could she be sure they were trustworthy? 'I'm doing my best,' she replied stiffly, trying to still her twisting fingers. 'It's only natural that I should feel a little—apprehensive.'

'Natural be damned!' he retorted explosively, looking swiftly across at her, his eyes darkened with anger. 'You're being deliberately awkward. What is it, have you made up your mind to make this day as big a disaster as you can? Is it your way of trying to prove that we are incompatible? Only children play stupid games like that. I credit you with more sense.'

Inwardly seething, Amber tried to make her voice pleasant. 'If you could see things from my point of view you might understand. You've told me nothing about yourself, yet I'm supposed to—to trust you. How can that be? How do I know that you're not going to carry me off somewhere and molest me?'

'Now you are being melodramatic.' Hamed's voice gave away none of his feelings. He drove smoothly and effortlessly along the wide straight road, sounding his horn at frequent intervals at cyclists and hippomobiles, or men on laden donkeys that looked too small to carry the load expected of them. 'If you had really thought that you would not have come.'

'I'm beginning to wish I hadn't,' she snapped, 'if we're going to argue all day. Besides, you blackmailed me into agreeing.'

'Then perhaps it's more blackmail we need now.' He slid the big car to a halt. 'I am never averse to kissing a pretty woman and you, my little passion flower, are very desirable. Did you not know that?'

Amber shrank into the corner of her seat trying to resist as he pulled her relentlessly towards him, but once his mouth found hers it was all over. The now familiar warmth sprang every nerve-end into life, her whole body became vibrantly alive. She tried to suppress these feelings, to remain unresponsive in his arms.

For a few seconds she succeeded until, weakened by his touch, she succumbed. A heady excitement coursed through her as she responded to his kiss, her lips parted willingly, her hands creeping round his back and holding him tight.

'Very, very desirable,' he continued thickly as he gently released her. 'Was that sufficient to persuade you that you are going to enjoy your day out?'

Amber nodded, her eyes starry. For the moment she was unable to shake off the languor induced by his kisses. All she wanted was to sit back in her seat with her eyes closed and remember the feel of his lips against hers. Involuntarily her fingers fluttered to her mouth and there flashed before her mind's eye a picture of the first time he had kissed her and she had washed every trace of it away. Now she wanted to cherish the memory even though at the same time she knew she should be angry with herself for responding. No doubt that would come later. Now she was living in a new world—a world where the slightest touch of this man sent her senses reeling.

The car moved slowly forward and it was a few minutes later before Amber opened her eyes. The self-satisfied smile on Hamed's face shook her and she sat suddenly upright. What had been to her a moving experience had meant no more to him than a successful experiment. He had used her again, used his undoubted masculine charm to get his own way.

She was about to tell him exactly what she thought of him when his hand came out and touched her own —and even that was enough to excite her emotions, to bring a weakness to her limbs. While despising her reaction Amber allowed her hand to remain in his, even going so far as to stroke it, noticing idly the scattering of fine dark hairs and the immaculately manicured nails. They were strong hands, hands capable of many things. She coloured at the line her thoughts were taking and released him abruptly, ignoring his swift questioning glance and staring out at the road ahead.

They bypassed Sousse with its memories of that first meeting and were soon heading along the main highway towards the capital. Eucalyptus trees stood like sentinels on each side of the road. Hamed told her that the Arabs tied bunches of eucalyptus to their houses to help keep away the flies.

They passed through villages where low whitewashed houses huddled together, where scores of children played, or sat on the roadside watching the traffic go by. 'Why aren't they at school?' asked Amber, curious as to why so many of them seemed to have nothing to do.

He said, 'There are not enough schools or teachers for all the children, so half of them go in the morning and the other half in the afternoon,' continuing proudly, 'We are a young and growing country. I expect you've noticed that the older people are in a minority. Over half of the population are aged under twenty.'

Amber found this information fascinating, indeed the whole country was casting a spell over her and she looked about her, anxious to miss nothing.

'This is the Sahel region,' announced Hamed a few miles further on. To their right and left stretched olive groves for as far as the eye could see. 'Next month the olives will be gathered—it is one of our biggest industries—and everyone, men, women and children, helps pick the fruit. For some it is the only season they can get work, so they are always very keen.'

The silvery trees shivered in the light breeze. There were miles and miles of them and Amber could imagine they would need all the help they could get to harvest the fruit.

Once out of the Sahel the countryside became barren with only the occasional village to break it up. There was always plenty of activity, though, whether it was a dark-skinned Arab tilling his tiny patch of earth or herding a handful of skinny-looking sheep along the roadside, or the women in their white *sifsaris* carrying enormous loads of shopping. Outside the butchers' shops, which often were no more than a shack on the roadside, were impaled cows' heads. This made Amber shudder, but she conveyed none of her thoughts to the man at her side. He seemed content to drive in silence, only occasionally drawing her attention to something he thought might interest her.

At last they reached the outskirts of Tunis, driving beside the lake, El-Bahira, which he told her meant, 'Little Sea', where a flock of flamingoes made a cheerful splash of colour against the grey water, and into the city itself.

Hamed parked his car and they walked along the main Avenue Habib Bourguiba, so called after the President, with its double row of palms down the middle and abundant with cafés, cinemas and travel agencies. Hamed stopped at the Centre de l'Artisanat, a large shop which carried a vast range of Tunisian handicrafts. 'There is no bargaining here,' he said with a smile, as they looked round with interest at the carpets and shawls, kaftans and the charming blue and white birdcages so popular in Tunisia.

Amber had so far remained silent, still unsure of her relationship with Hamed, but now, looking at a rack of colourful kaftans, she exclaimed, 'Oh, isn't this beautiful!' The deep sea green was decorated with rich golden embroidery and she knew instinctively that the colour would suit her.

Almost before she knew it Hamed had bought the gown and handed the parcel to her with a mocking bow. 'For my passion flower. A present from Tunis to make her feel at home.'

Scarlet flamed her cheeks. No man had ever bought her a present before—and for it to be this stranger! She hoped he had not thought she was hinting.

'You shouldn't,' she exclaimed hotly. 'I never meant you to—I didn't realise—— Oh, please, take it back!'

He placed a gentle finger on her lips, smiling in an oddly persuasive manner. 'It is my pleasure and I shall be most hurt if you do not accept.' His fingers closed on her bare arm and he led her forcibly from the shop. Even outside he did not relax his grip and Amber thought it would be ungrateful if she shrugged herself loose. But the close contact caused her pulses to race once again. His hand was warm on her arm, warm and slightly possessive. She wondered whether he was attempting to buy himself into her favour, wishing she had been more adamant in refusing the dress. He certainly seemed more possessive, while she herself— how did she feel? Confused and slightly breathless, yet not altogether unhappy. A strange state of affairs. It was this alien side to her nature which was letting her down—a side which was becoming more predominant with each passing hour.

Next door to the Artisanat was the Municipal Theatre, a lovely white building with steps leading down to it upon which many people sat and rested. Directly opposite was a colourful flower market and further along still the American Cultural Center where a fountain played in a shady courtyard.

Hamed pointed out the neo-gothic Cathedral of St Vincent de Paul where many tourists stood taking photographs of its gold mosaic-studded façade. There was a mural of Christ surrounded by angels and above that two domed towers, a familiar part of the Tunis skyline.

They stopped at a café and had a long cooling drink before carrying on to the entrance of the medina, through the ancient gate, Bab el Bahar. 'It means sea-gate,' explained Hamed. 'In mediaeval times the salt waters of El-Bahira came right up to here. There is a story that a certain Baroness Fasciotti who lived on the lakeside used to pay the dustmen to dump their rubbish in the shallows. This continued over the centuries until now it is all built up between here and the lake, which, I believe, is still receding.'

'It's difficult to imagine,' said Amber, 'that this all used to be water.' She turned and looked back along the avenue. 'It's all so—so solid—so very much a part of Tunis.' And then she looked again at the 'sea-gate' with its iron ladder up one side and tattered posters on its crumbling masonry, 'and the medina, I suppose, was the original city?'

Hamed nodded. 'Do you want to look around the souks? I promise to keep close by your side. I won't let any ardent young man run away with you.'

Although he teased Amber did not mind. She was

learning to relax in Hamed's presence, sometimes forgetting that she knew nothing about him. His English was so perfect and his colouring only a little darker than her own so that she could even forget he was of Arabian blood. She nodded and together they walked along the main street of the medina.

'This is different from Sousse,' he said. 'There are many lanes and it is easy to get lost.'

'Then I'll stick close by your side,' smiled Amber, glad now of his protective arm. They stopped and watched an engraver hammering out tourists' names on brass ashtrays which were already decorated but had room left at the bottom. The engraver had a flower tucked behind one ear and wore the traditional red *chechia* on his head. He was a cheerful man and Amber was delighted when Hamed bought her an ashtray with her name in Arabic. It was a beautiful flowing writing and although she could never begin to understand it she knew she would always treasure this souvenir of her holiday in Tunisia.

But even more beautiful still was the sand rose he gave her. 'It's called a desert rose,' he said. 'They are created from small pieces of rock by the desert winds cutting away the soft sand and leaving only a hard core with these petals that look so much like roses.'

Amber was entranced. She had never seen anything quite so lovely, and the fact that it was created by nature herself made it all the more appealing.

Constant bargaining went on on either side of them, fathers taught their sons their trade, brasses gleamed, coloured rugs and carpets added colour, perfumes filled the air with their haunting fragrance and the smell of spice tempted them. With Hamed at her side Amber felt safe. She could laugh now at her experience in the souks in Sousse, but it had been her first encounter with Tunisian markets and she felt she could be excused. The Arabs meant no harm—it was just their way of conducting business. Even so she kept close to Hamed's side, aware that many eyes were drawn her way and that it was not always an accident when a brown hand brushed her body.

They ate lunch at the Hotel Africa and afterwards drove to Belvedere Park, a wooded hill overlooking the city. They left the car and walked through the grounds where flowering shrubs made brilliant splashes of colour. Hamed picked a crimson flower and tucked it behind her ear, saying softly, 'The hibiscus, it means a sign of great love.'

Amber had felt flattered, but now she tore it away and flung it to the ground. 'I hardly think that applies to us!'

But he only laughed and they continued walking. They explored the Kouba, a blue and white pavilion with ceilings and arches of delicately carved stucco, and marble pillars decorated with scrolls and crescents. Marble seats linked the arches and here they sat for a while.

'It will soon be time for us to return,' said Hamed. 'Have you had a pleasant day? Did it hold any of the terrors you anticipated?'

Amber shook her head, smiling wryly, forgetting the incident of the flower. 'I'm sorry, I misjudged you. I've really enjoyed myself. I wouldn't have missed it for anything.'

'Then you will come out with me again?' He watched her face intently as if her answer was important to him.

'You're rushing me,' countered Amber. 'I'll have to think about it.' She would have liked to agree, but once again uncertainty took over.

'With only one more week of your holiday left it is necessary for me to work quickly if I want to see anything of you,' argued Hamed. 'Please, Amber, don't deny me the pleasure of your company.'

He knew so much about her, but once again doubts filled Amber's mind. 'I'll give you your answer when we get back to the Sahara Beach,' she said positively. Meantime she would question him and endeavour to find out something about this determined man.

They sat in silence for a few moments before Hamed sprang suddenly to his feet, his eyes cool and his lips thinned. He held out his hand. 'Come, let us get back to the car.'

It seemed he was offended by her indecision. Either that or he was impatient for her answer and wanted to get back as quickly as possible. Amber gave a mental shrug and ignoring his outstretched arm gathered up her parcels and rose to stand at his side. He could please himself. If he was going to be funny with her she would definitely refuse to go out with him again. He had been excellent company all day and she had really thought she was beginning to like him. Now, with those dark eyes regarding her coldly, she had her doubts.

He drove fast, braking so violently at times that had it not been for her seat belt she would have found herself thrust forward against the windscreen. 'What's the matter?' she asked at last, unable to stand the oppressive silence any longer. 'Are you so eager for my decision that you can't wait to get back?'

'It has nothing to do with it.' He spoke tonelessly, all his attention on the grey ribbon of road ahead, cursing harshly in Arabic when he was compelled to let a young boy, a dog and three sheep cross the road.

'Then why the bad mood?' persisted Amber.

'It is your inability to give me a direct answer that angers me. Why do you always prevaricate when you know you will say yes in the end?' He allowed his eyes to leave the road for one moment to rest darkly on her. They were blacker than she had ever known, hooded by heavy lids and thick beetling brows. It was impossible to read his expression, though his mouth was firm and that tell-tale pulse beat high in his jaw.

'You sound very sure of yourself.' A spurt of anger hardened her voice. 'Too damned sure for my liking.' It was very rarely she swore, but today was an exception. She was suddenly so angry she did not care what she said. 'Well, you can have your answer now, and it's *no*. I don't care to keep company with a man who gets into evil black moods for no reason at all.' Her heart was racing as erratically as when he had kissed her—but her passion now was violated by fury, not excitement.

For several long moments there was silence between them, a deep tangible silence that filled the car, making Amber more tense with every second that passed. Hamed's foot went down on the accelerator and Amber, who had thought he was already going flat out, felt the car surge forward at an even more alarming rate. She wanted to cry out but knew that to do so would add fuel to his already heightened temper.

People and villages flew by and she closed her eyes, convinced they would have an accident, while at the same time grudgingly admiring the way he handled the car. It was as though it was part of him. He knew his own and the vehicle's capabilities and so far as he was concerned there was no danger. It was only Amber who feared for her life. At last she could stand it no longer. 'For goodness' sake,' she exclaimed, 'are you trying to get us both killed?'

'Scared, are you?' he mocked, 'Perhaps it will make you change your mind. Your destiny lies in your own hands.'

'You mean——' Amber's golden eyes widened incredulously, 'this is another form of blackmail? Well, let me tell you, *Mr* Slouma, I don't like your methods of persuasion. They're despicable!' She was breathing rapidly now, for the moment forgetting they were in the car and that she ought not to be distracting his attention. 'If you think I'm going to change my mind you're very much mistaken. I wouldn't go out with you again if you were the last man on earth!'

He seemed amused, a smile flickering on his lips, though it was impossible to read his true expression since he kept his eyes on the road. 'You may have to take back those words, my passionate one. If I were you I would think very carefully before I speak.'

'What do you mean? You can't make me see you again. I've had enough of you and your moods. Next time I date a man I shall make certain he's placid and peaceful.'

'He would not suit you.' Still that aggravating smile. 'You need a man of fire and passion. Have you not found that out? Do not tell me my kisses have not stirred your blood—for I know it is true. The type of man you mention would do nothing for you—his lovemaking would be as passionless as his nature. You need me, Amber. Your body responds to mine even though you are ready to deny it. Do you not believe in fate. We were destined to meet, you and I, and now I have found you I am never going to let you go.'

A prickle of fear ran down Amber's spine. He sounded so confident. There was no doubt in his mind that he spoke the truth. But how could he accomplish this unless she herself agreed?

Almost as if in answer to her unspoken question Hamed slowed down and swung the car off the road on to what was little more than a narrow dirt track. Panic rose in Amber's throat, threatening to choke her. This was not the way they had come. Where was he taking her? What was he going to do? '*Stop!*' she shrieked, almost unable to recognise her own voice. It sounded high-pitched and frightened. She *was* frightened. Her palms were moist and she held them against her ears as if trying to shut out this terrible thing that was happening to her. 'Hamed—where are you taking me? I demand that you stop, that you turn round right now and take me back to the hotel!'

He still drove fast, though there was not the necessity now for him to give all his attention to the road. His head turned towards her and he smiled, his slightly uneven teeth showing up with startling whiteness against his tanned skin. 'Do not be afraid. I am going to show you my house.'

But to Amber that smile held menace and though his voice was soft she knew he would not yield. He was hard, all through; a ruthless man, determined to possess her, and who would let nothing stand in his way. Why, oh, why had she agreed to come out with him today? Why hadn't she found out more about him before allowing herself to become involved? All along she had had doubts—had felt that there was some ulterior motive behind his friendship—and now she knew. He was kidnapping her. She would never be seen by her friends again.

What had he in mind? she wondered. Was she to be his plaything? He had made no secret of the fact that he found her body desirable—and she, her cheeks flamed at the thought, had responded. Was it because he knew what he could do to her? Was he perhaps taking her home to satisfy his own erotic desires? Was he, like the Arabs he had warned her of, attracted by the fairness of her hair and when all other methods had failed had seen this as the only way to get her to himself?

Her mind was a turmoil, thoughts racing chaotically inside her head. They were driving through an orange grove, the fruit already ripening on the trees, but Amber paid scant attention to her surroundings. If she did not escape now it would be too late. Dared she risk throwing herself from the car? But where could she run? His long legs would soon catch up with her. It appeared there was no way out; she must accept what fate held in store. But not without a fight!

The trees thinned and the road curved and suddenly straight in front of them, was an immense white villa. Many of the houses she had seen had been little more than squat white buildings, though occasionally there had been better class houses with gardens and flowers, but these had been in the minority. The one facing her now was like nothing else she had seen. It was so beautiful it took her breath away and for a few seconds she forgot to be angry.

The roof was domed and below it were several windows and doors leading out on to a terrace. This was reached by curved staircases on either side and supported by arabesque arches. Through the ornamental arches was a large entrance door painted blue and studded with black nails in an intricate pattern. Round the edge of the terrace were wrought iron railings, also painted blue, and covering each window a picturesque 'half-fig' of wrought iron, which Amber knew was called a *mashrabia* and had once been used as a sort of blind from which cloistered wives could see but not be seen. Blue and white were colours predominantly used in Tunisia—white to combat the heat and blue to repel the flies. Domes helped the air circulate inside.

It was a few moments before Amber realised that the car had stopped and Hamed was holding open her door. Reality returned. 'If you're expecting to take me inside,' she snapped, 'you're mistaken!'

One thick brow quirked. 'You are not impressed by my house. I thought you woud find it fascinating.'

'It looks very beautiful,' said Amber politely, 'but I'm more interested in getting back to the hotel than admiring where you live.'

'A pity.' His eyes became flint-like. 'Because I intend taking you inside.'

Amber remained firmly seated. 'Then you'll have to carry me, because I shan't go in of my own free will.'

'You think I wouldn't?' Almost before he had finished speaking Hamed bent down and sliding one arm beneath her knees and the other round her back he lifted her effortlessly. When she struggled he grinned. 'My little passion flower is fighting. That is good. I should not like you to become submissive.'

'Oh, I hate you!' spat Amber, trying in vain to free herself. 'You won't get away with this. I shall see that you're punished. Men like you deserve to be put in prison!'

'What have I done?' he asked in mock innocence, 'I have invited you to my home. What harm is there in that?'

'Invited?' screamed Amber. 'You've forced me here against my will.'

'It is your word against mine, my little one. I am a respected man. I know who they will believe.'

'So you say, but you've told me nothing about yourself. For all I know this might not even be your house. You're probably just a servant here.' She was speaking irrationally and knew it, but anger drove her on. 'If you're so important tell me who you are.'

For an answer he smiled enigmatically and kicked on the door. It was opened immediately by a small brown-skinned, surprisingly blue-eyed boy who could be any age between eleven and fifteen. Upon seeing Hamed he beamed and opened the door wider, speaking rapidly in his own language. He showed no surprise at Amber in Hamed's arms and she wondered whether this was not the first time this arrogant man had done this sort of thing. She would not put it past him. Perhaps he kept a harem and she was to become its latest member? Then she scoffed at herself for allowing her thoughts to run away. That sort of thing did not go on here, or at least she did not think it did!

Once the door had closed behind them Hamed put her down. 'This is Mohammed,' he said. 'One of my— servants.' He paused, waiting her reaction, but Amber kept her face impassive, not even allowing herself the vestige of a smile for this engaging young Arab. 'Mohammed, this is Miss Christy. Would you please get a room ready for her.'

The boy nodded and ran off grinning. Hamed took Amber's hand and would have led her forward had it not been for the fact that she wrenched herself free, stamping her foot on the mosaic tiled floor. Her eyes were wide and luminous and definitely apprehensive. 'A room?' she echoed indignantly, all her worst fears coming true. 'What do I want a room for. I'm not going to stay.'

'I thought you would want to freshen yourself up,' he said blandly, his arms folded across his broad chest, his head tipped to one side and an expression of amused pleasure softening his harsh features.

Amber studied him. 'I would like a wash, certainly,' she said guardedly, 'but I don't think that's what you meant. Nor did Mohammed.' It was humiliating to think that the boy should so eagerly have gone to prepare her room. What was going through his mind—did he think she was to become Hamed's concubine?

'No,' admitted Hamed at length. 'You are right—I do intend to keep you here.'

'For what reason?' Amber's heartbeats were increasing at an alarming rate. Her mouth was dry and she felt the blood pounding in her head. She pressed her hands to her temples. Not until this moment had the true horror of her situation struck her. 'You can't do

this. I'm going—I won't stay here a moment longer!'
She spun round and faced the door, wondering why
her head felt so peculiar. Perhaps it was the heat,
coupled with the total unreality of this last hour?

The walls began to recede and as if from a distance
she heard Hamed's voice:

'I brought you here because I am going to marry
you.'

CHAPTER FOUR

WHEN Amber came round it took her several seconds to realise what had happened and where she was. The room in which she found herself had a carved domed roof, exquisitely painted in gold. In contrast the walls were starkly white. The cover on the bed was hand-woven in shades of red, blue and purple; so too were the rugs on the floor. Carved furniture in dark polished wood stood against the walls—and beside the bed stood Hamed.

She looked up into his dark anxious face, wondering whether she had really heard those words or whether it had all been a figment of her imagination.

'W-what did you say?' she whispered, struggling to rise and resisting strongly when he pushed her back down.

'That I am going to marry you.' He placed a hand on the pillow each side of her head, lowering his body until his face was alarmingly close. Those powerful dark eyes held her mesmerised, daring her to dispute him.

'That's what I thought you said.' Her voice shook with suppressed emotion. 'You must be mad! You can't go around making rash statements like that. Doesn't it matter what I feel, what I want to do?' she ended hysterically, feeling very near to tears and wondering exactly how she was going to get out of this situation. She was no match for Hamed, that much she knew.

Slowly he shook his head. 'Not one little bit, at least not until I allow you to voice your opinion. You are now mine and very shortly you will be my wife.'

The face above her leered into a smile. Amber put up her hands and pushed with all her strength, convinced it was the devil himself who had come to torment her. Those evil eyes blazing into her own surely meant nothing but harm?

But against Hamed's much greater strength she was pitifully weak. He caught her hands and raised them to his lips, pressing a kiss into each palm before enfolding them in his own. 'My sweet Amber, how lovely you are when you're cross. Your eyes shine like jewels. Do you know they are one of the first things I noticed about you? Such an unusual colour—like a tiger's.'

He was temporarily relaxed and Amber snatched her hands free, dragging her nails down his cheek and feeling a great sense of satisfaction at the red streaks which became immediately apparent. 'I can also scratch like a tiger,' she spat. 'If you insist on this ridiculous idea of keeping me here you'll find me a very wild animal indeed! I don't like being told what I'm going to do, and I shall resist you strongly. You might find you'll regret your decision and wish you'd never brought me here!'

Hamed touched his cheek, frowning at the trace of blood on his fingertips. Pulling a handkerchief from his pocket he wiped them clean, dabbing ineffectually at his cheek, for the thin lines of blood had already dried. 'I think that extremely unlikely,' he said, 'but if you know what is good for you you will not attempt to hurt me again. This time I will forget it, but another time I shall not be so lenient.'

'And what will the great master do,' cried Amber passionately, 'give me forty strokes of the whip and lock me in a cell? You're a barbarian and I hate you, I hate you, *I hate you!*' Tears raced down her cheeks. She felt as though she was going out of her mind. Why had she ever left England? Why had she let Dr Greer persuade her that she needed a holiday? It was like a nightmare from which there was no escape. If only she could wake up and find it had all been a dream! She closed her eyes and opened them again. Hamed Ben Slouma was still there, blurred by her tears but very much alive and very much a part of these nerve-racking circumstances.

'I think not, my little wildcat. How can you say you hate me when I have only to touch you to have you melt in my arms?'

'Not now that I know what sort of a man you are.' Amber struggled from the bed and stood facing him, her breathing deep and erratic, her golden eyes sparkling in anger. 'You're despicable! You'll never get away with this. I shall find some way to get my own back.'

Her threat appeared to amuse him, for his lips quirked as he said, 'I think not, my little one, though it will be interesting to see what you plan to do. My own methods, though, are much more likely to meet with success.'

Before Amber had time to retreat he stepped forward, placing one firm brown hand on each cheek— his touch warm and gentle, but at the same time firm.

When she tried to pull back it was to no avail. He drew inexorably closer, his eyes never leaving her face.

Amber trembled, despising herself for the weakness which flowed through her limbs, determined that he should not see the effect he had on her. 'Leave me alone,' she cried. 'Don't touch me!'

But he smiled aggravatingly, his thumbs stroking her cheeks in an entirely sensuous manner. 'Are you afraid of yourself?' he mocked. 'Afraid of the feelings my touch evokes? Do not deny it. Your body gives you away. My sweet Amber, you are so vulnerable, so innocent.' His thumb touched the corner of her mouth, parting her lips, 'and so very desirable.'

And he desired her! It was registered in his face. Fearfully Amber ran the tip of her tongue over suddenly dry lips in an unconsciously provocative gesture.

Hamed groaned and closed his mouth on hers, his lips firm and demanding against her soft moistness. Feeling herself drowning in a tide of emotion, Amber knew she must resist, summon up every ounce of willpower to deny this man. Otherwise all would be lost. He could not make her marry him against her will, she was sure of that, but he could keep her here—and use her to satisfy his own desires. This thought brought strength to her limbs and raising her hands to his chest she pushed with all her strength. Beneath her fingers his heart beat strongly, but he did not move. Instead he lifted his mouth and laughed triumphantly.

'It is no use trying to escape. You belong to me now. You are mine to do with as I like, and at this moment I want to kiss you very thoroughly.'

Amber shook her head in anguish. 'You're crazy! I don't belong to you.'

He shrugged. 'We shall soon be married. What do a few days matter?'

'To me they make all the difference,' she snapped. 'Let me go at once, you—you blackguard!'

But his arms slid round her back, pulling her close. His lips sought the hollow of her throat, his kisses burning into her skin until it was all she could do to stop herself arching her body towards him in a gesture of surrender. His teeth and tongue teased as he moved his head upwards, gently biting the lobe of her ear before once again seeking her mouth, ravaging her senses so that she felt confused by the sheer magnitude of her feelings. Her physical awareness of him grew each time he touched her. It was like a white-hot fire burning inside, something over which she had no control.

The most damning part of this was that he knew. As surely as if she had told him he knew exactly what his kisses did to her—and enjoyed the power it gave him. His mouth moved again to her throat, one hand cupping the rounded fullness of her breast. 'Hamed, no——' began Amber, knowing she should stop him, but threatened by a weakness which filled every limb. Her head spun as his touch sent spirals of ecstasy cavorting round her body. 'Please——'

His mouth effectively stemmed her half-hearted protest and she knew she had lost. Her appetite whetted and hungry now for his love, she pressed her body close to his, feeling his hard muscular thighs against hers, aware of the urgency of his body. Her hands crept round the back of his neck, pulling his head closer. Sane reasoning departed. Every inch of her craved for his touch. This wanting a man was an entirely new feeling for Amber. Never before had she felt so shame-less, so entirely without self-respect. Her lips moved against his, inviting, appealing.

'Amber,' he breathed hoarsely, picking her up and carrying her across to the bed.

It was not until he began to undo the buttons on the front of her dress that Amber came to her senses and her eyes widened in shocked dismay. What had she been thinking? How could she have cheapened herself to such an extent as to let this man think that he could—her cheeks flamed, unable even to voice to herself what he might have done. 'No, Hamed, no!' she exclaimed wildly, trying to fight off his urgent hands.

He stopped abruptly, a frown darkening his hand-some face. 'What is this? What kind of a woman are you to stop me now? I did not notice you resisting a few moments ago.'

'I didn't know what I was doing. I must have been mad to let you touch me!'

'No, not mad,' he said calmly, 'merely feminine. You cannot help yourself, so why try to fight what you most desire?'

Amber's eyes flashed angrily. 'You conceited pig! How dare you assume to know what I feel! If I wanted you do you think I would be pushing you away now?'

'A token resistance,' came the smooth reply.

The fact that her temper had no effect on him out-raged her even further. 'Is that what you think? Well, let me tell you, Mr High and Mighty Slouma, the feel of your hands on my body makes my skin crawl! I merely gave in to you because—well, because I thought it would be the easiest way out.'

His eyes narrowed. 'And when you found things were getting a little out of hand you panicked. Is that what you're trying to tell me?' And as she nodded he continued, 'Well, let me now tell you something. I am no innocent when it comes to women—so you are either a superb actress or you are lying. I tend to think it is the latter. I am tempted to find out—but you have earned your reprieve,' he lifted himself from the bed and stood surveying her, an odd light in his dark eyes, 'for the time being. Perhaps you would like to wash and change before joining me downstairs. You will find plenty of clothes in the wardrobe, all of which are your size.'

Amber gasped, her eyes flickering to the huge cupboard and back towards Hamed, but he was already leaving the room. When the door closed behind him she sat up, her eyes wide with apprehension. He must have planned this down to the last detail if he had gone to the trouble of supplying her with clothes—unless he entertained frequently. A thought which surprisingly she found distasteful.

Curiosity now got the better of her and she crossed the room and swung open the heavy door, catching her breath in wonder at the fine array of dresses. There were clothes to suit every occasion—evening dresses, day dresses, skirts, blouses, even trousers—and on the shelves at the side were shorts and tops, swimwear. A drawer in the dresser revealed exquisite undergarments, lace bras and delicate matching briefs—all of which were her size exactly. How he had known she had no idea, unless his experience with women had enabled him to assess her size accurately. Her cheeks flushed at the thought of Hamed choosing these intimate garments and she felt like tearing each one into shreds. It would do her no good, though, she acknowledged resignedly. The best she could do would be to appear to accept the situation and hope she could find some way of escaping before he carried out his threat to marry her.

A bathroom led off her bedroom, exquisite in summer blue with jade towels adding bold colour. It looked cool and restful, and the thought of lying for a few minutes in warm perfumed water appealed instantly to Amber. It would help relieve her inner tension, though she was sure nothing could take away the numbness which had settled around her heart.

She was disturbed to find there were no locks on any of the doors and her heart beat just a little quicker as she slipped out of her clothes. The water caressed her skin like silk and closing her eyes she could almost forget the horror of her situation. This was such a beautiful house it was a pity that she had been brought here under protest. At any other time she would have been enchanted. It was far more luxurious than anything else she had ever known. But the thought that at any moment Hamed could walk in was sufficiently disturbing to stop her from lingering in the bath.

She dressed in a pretty, short cotton dress in the palest of greens. It fitted her perfectly. It was simple, yet she knew instinctively it had cost a lot of money and her brow furrowed as to why he should go to so much trouble and expense on her behalf. Right from the beginning of their association he had puzzled her. There was so much he knew about her, yet he was remarkably reticent about himself. Why? Had he something to hide—or was there some perfectly simple explanation? If there was she would like to know.

The sun had tanned her skin to honey gold and she needed no make-up. The face that looked back in the mirror revealed none of her inner torment. She looked a happy, carefree girl enjoying her holiday in the sun. Her fair hair was several shades lighter than when she had arrived and she brushed it now until it lay like silk about her shoulders. She knew she was attractive, but not exceptionally so that Hamed should single her out. Her frown returned as she slipped her feet into a pair of white high-heeled sandals and opened the door.

Outside in the corridor she stopped, unsure which way to go, but she had walked no more than a few steps when Hamed appeared. His easy smile caused her heart to flip, while at the same time she despised herself for allowing these feelings to surface. She permitted no answering smile to soften her lips, holding her head aloof as she walked towards him.

Her action did not go unnoticed. 'You are so much prettier when you smile,' he said, 'and the dress is perfect. The colour complements your honey-coloured hair and those cat-like eyes. Why spoil the effect? Are you still angry with me?' The scratches on his cheek were hardly noticeable now, but his bright eyes showed that he had neither forgotten nor forgiven.

'Until you let me go I shall never be otherwise,' retorted Amber coolly. 'What do you expect me to do—jump for joy that I'm receiving the undivided attention of a rich and handsome man?'

'What makes you think I am rich?' He draped a hand carelessly about her shoulders, leading her forward to the white-painted staircase which had suddenly come into view.

'All this,' she said, with an expressive wave of one hand, trying to shrug herself free only to find his grip tightening, 'and the fact that you can apparently afford to buy me a whole wardrobe of clothes—unless you always keep them there for just such emergencies?'

His lips quirked. 'Would it bother you to think I did?'

'Not in the least,' lied Amber, 'nor would it surprise me to discover you make a habit of this sort of thing.'

'I am sorry you have such a low opinion,' he said softly. 'I'm not really so bad as you think—if you would only allow yourself the chance to find out.'

'The chance!' scoffed Amber. 'Nothing you've yet done or said has given me reason to have confidence in you. You apparently knew all about me before you conveniently *rescued* me in the medina, yet you refuse to disclose your interest. Was it your plan then to marry me? Was that your ultimate aim?' Stiff with anger, she turned at the bottom of the stairs, glaring at Hamed, daring him to refute her statement.

'My sweet one,' he said, completely indifferent to her temper, 'would you believe me if I said no? Of course you wouldn't, not in the mood you are in now. Come, we will take a drink and then I will show you my house.'

The room he ushered her into was carpeted in thick white fur, but there were no chairs, merely large cushions placed on the floor. In front of them were low tables, pinned on the white walls were woven rugs and in a corner stood an open-fronted cabinet well stocked with drinks.

Amber could not help exclaiming aloud at the

simple yet effective furnishings.

'You like it?' he asked, looking pleased. 'A typical Tunisian room. The rest of my house has European furniture, but I like to keep this room for my special guests. It helps them feel they are sampling my way of life.'

Amber lowered herself on to one of the full, soft cushions. 'You speak very good English. It's sometimes difficult to believe you're an Arab.'

He handed her a glass filled with pale, almost white, wine. 'I was educated in England. Indeed I had many happy years there. My maternal grandparents were English and I spent most of my youth with them.'

'Are they still alive?' At last she was learning something about this man who had so dramatically altered her whole life.

'No, I am afraid not—nor my parents—and as I was an only child you could say I am alone in the world. We are two of a kind, you and I, both alone, both needing company. A perfect situation, don't you think?' He lowered himself on to a cushion at her side, leaning forward, awaiting her answer.

'The hell I do,' snapped Amber. 'I don't know how you know so much about me, but you're mistaken if you think my being parentless makes me easy game for you. If and when I decide to marry it will certainly be to no one like you. I prefer to make my own decisions, not have them made for me.'

He sipped his drink and studied her with open amusement. 'It is a pity you think the way you do. It will make my task twice as hard—*persuading* you that I am the right man to be your husband.'

'If you ask me,' persisted Amber, 'I would say it's an

impossible task. I shall never agree, *never*. So you may as well give up now and take me back to my hotel. Does it not bother you that my friends will wonder what's happened when I don't turn up this evening?'

He shrugged laconically. 'Why should it? You are my only concern. Tomorrow your luggage will be delivered here and then there will be nothing left for you to worry about.'

The casualness with which he made this statement enraged Amber even further. She swallowed her drink in one mouthful and struggled to her feet, bursting into a torrent of angry words. 'That's the last straw! This time you've gone too far. How dare you condescend to take over my affairs! I demand that you take me back to the Sahara Beach right now.' She stamped one elegant foot on the thick carpet. '*Now*, do you hear! I will not remain in your house one moment longer!'

Slowly and effortlessly he hauled himself up. 'You are wasting your breath, my sweet one. My plans are made.' A trace of laughter still lingered on his lips and his dark eyes probed her body as though he would like nothing more at that moment than to make love. 'Whether you agree or not I intend to make you mine. I want you more than any other woman I have met, and rest assured I always get what I want.' He stepped forward and Amber found herself powerless to move, even though instinct told her what he was going to do.

With a gentleness strange for so big a man Hamed touched her cheek. 'You are so beautiful, my passion flower. Can you not understand why it is that I desire you? You are like a breath of my beloved England come back to me.' His eyes narrowed as his hand moved slowly down her throat and with a sudden savage movement he drew her to him.

Amber closed her eyes, letting herself go limp. To resist would get her nowhere—besides, she could not deny the clamouring of her pulses. There emanated from Hamed a magnetism that any woman would find hard to deny. His strong personal charm overrode any anger she might feel. She was as malleable as putty in his hands even though she knew it was imperative she try to keep hidden her attraction towards him. Strong as it might be, she had a certain code of ethics and a man who treated her as had Hamed today did not deserve to have a woman fall into his arms.

'Amber, Amber,' breathed Hamed hoarsely in her ear, 'why do you deny me what I know you want to give? Why do you pretend that my embrace means nothing to you?'

The intensity in his voice caused a tremor to run through Amber but she did not relax in her determination not to give in. 'I'm not pretending. I despise men who take advantage of a woman. It's not fair, and if you insist on keeping me here against my will you'll soon find I'm not the acquiescent partner you hoped for. I shall fight you every inch of the way!'

As she spoke he pushed her away until she was held at arm's length. 'You are reckoning without my expertise. In a few days you will wonder why you ever resisted me. In case you are not aware of it, Amber, I do know how to treat a woman, and to me you are something special.'

'If you really meant that you wouldn't hurt me.' To no avail she tried to pull away from his inflexible grip.

'It is sometimes necessary to hurt those very dear to you,' returned Hamed, making no attempt to release her. 'There is no other way in which they will see reason.'

Amber tossed her head scornfully. 'Are you trying to tell me that every time I refuse to fall in with your wishes you're going to inflict physical punishment? Are you a sadist, as well as all the other things I would like to call you?'

'I hope that will not be necessary,' he returned calmly. 'I do not make a habit of hurting women.'

'No doubt they all fall into your arms with absolutely no persuasion,' she said drily.

'I must admit I do not usually have difficulty,' admitted Hamed, 'but I must also be perfectly frank and say that I have never found myself in exactly these circumstances before. You are the only woman I have ever wanted to marry.'

For one second as he looked at her his fingers relaxed and Amber took the opportunity to swing away from him. 'If I'm supposed to be flattered, you're going to be disappointed!'

To her surprise he laughed. 'Come, I will show you over the house and gardens. It will perhaps give your temper time to cool, and who knows, you may be a little more affable over dinner.'

CHAPTER FIVE

DINNER was not the cosy twosome Hamed had planned. They had an unexpected guest. She had joined them earlier in the garden and Amber had been immediately aware that he was not at all pleased by the intrusion.

He had introduced her as Rafika, a pretty Tunisian girl aged about sixteen, who, in common with most of the youngsters, was dressed in Western-style clothes. Her dark hair hung long and straight about her shoulders and her wide brown eyes looked coolly at the blonde English girl, a tiny frown marring the smooth perfection of her forehead.

'You are a business friend of Hamed's?' she had asked, in English that was only slightly less perfect than that of the man whose arm she had possessively taken.

But before Amber could answer Hamed himself had said, 'Amber is—my fiancée.'

Rafika's beautiful eyes had hardened, but she smiled, stiffly, politely, 'Let me be the first to congratulate you,' and she lifted her chin, kissing Hamed's cheek before bestowing a perfunctory smile on Amber. 'When did all this happen?'

Extricating himself from Rafika's embrace, Hamed placed an arm lightly about Amber's shoulders, smiling fondly down. 'We only met a few days ago. Amber is holidaying here.'

73

'So—it would appear to be love at first sight?' Rafika's remarks were directed towards Amber. 'I trust you know what you are doing. Our ways are very different from yours.'

'Rafika!' Hamed spoke sharply and the dark girl immediately looked embarrassed.

'I'm sorry, Hamed,' she said softly, lowering her thick lashes and resting one hand on his arm. 'I cannot help it if I am jealous. I always thought that one day——'

Hamed dashed her hand away impatiently. 'You know perfectly well my feelings towards you.' He added something in Arabic and Rafika retorted hotly, but after that the girl was perfectly civil towards Amber, even though Amber herself was aware of an underlying hostility.

When it was time to change for dinner Hamed requested Amber to wear the kaftan he had bought her in Tunis. She had been tempted to disregard his wishes, but the thought of facing his anger in front of Rafika was sufficient to persuade her that on this occasion at least she would do as he said.

The deep sea green suited her, as she had known it would, and she turned this way and that in front of the mirror, pleased with the reflection she saw. The garment made her feel feminine in a way she had not expected and there was a lightness to her step as she made her way down to the dining room.

Rafika and Hamed were already there, standing at the far end, each holding a glass of red wine, speaking softly in Arabic, and for a few seconds Amber was able to watch them unobserved. Rafika looked very happy, laughing up into Hamed's face, apparently all her earlier annoyance having disappeared. She still wore the same short dress with its matching jacket in which she had arrived, although her hair was freshly brushed and her face skilfully made up to enhance the sparkling depth of her lovely brown eyes and sensual lips. For one so young she certainly knew how to make the most of herself, thought Amber.

Hamed wore a dinner suit, his shirt startlingly white against his deeply tanned skin. Tall—and incredibly handsome—he made her heart skip a beat. Watching them it became apparent that Rafika was in love with him, though he had clearly felt no embarrassment in telling her that she meant nothing to him. She was much younger than he and he treated her as such, good-humouredly, like an older brother.

Suddenly, as of one accord, they turned, Hamed's smile widening when he saw Amber, but it was Rafika whom Amber watched and a shiver ran through her at the look of open hatred on the girl's face.

She had no time to dwell on this reaction, however, for Hamed strode swiftly forward and gathered her into his arms. 'Habibati, how exquisite you look! Rafika,' turning towards the other girl, 'do you not think the kaftan suits Amber?'

Rafika shrugged carelessly. 'Myself, I prefer Western clothes. If Amber wishes to dress up then that is up to her.' As she spoke the girl walked towards the table, hitching up her already short skirt, so that as she sat down and crossed her legs it revealed a provocative length of thigh.

Amber felt uncomfortable. Rafika's slighting reference to her dress made her wish that she had defied Hamed and worn something typically English. It was

as though they had both reversed their roles, the
strange part being that Rafika was completely at ease
whereas Amber herself felt distinctly out of place. The
kaftan suddenly felt all wrong on someone of her
colouring, as though she was trying to act a part that
did not suit her. But Hamed gave no indication that
he saw anything wrong and led Amber to the table, sitting her on his left hand, with Rafika on the right.

Amber toyed with her cutlery, only half listening as
Rafika talked about people and places of which she
herself had no knowledge. It might not have been so
bad had she been there of her own free will, but because she was a virtual prisoner it made things doubly
hard to bear. What would Rafika think, she wondered,
if she knew the true circumstances? Perhaps she
would not be so hostile if she learned that Amber was
being held here against her wishes. She could be a
useful ally. It was a thought worth thinking about, yet
would Rafika really help? She might value her friendship with Hamed too highly to risk getting involved
in anything that would warrant his anger. Amber
sighed unconsciously. This was almost certain to be
the case. Her problem was one she had to resolve herself.

A young black girl in a loose-fitting flowered skirt
and a vivid yellow blouse brought in their soup,
looking curiously at Amber from beneath lowered
lashes. Amber could guess at the speculation going on
inside the servant's head, but so deep was her distress
at this moment that all she could manage was a weak
smile.

'*Yubdarik Alldahuu feek*,' said Hamed as the girl
stood by to see whether anything else was required.

'That will be all for now.'

After they had spooned their soup in silence for a few minutes Hamed said, 'I trust you find the *shorba houd* to your liking? I have an excellent cook and you will find all the food in this house is first class.'

'It's very nice,' she said politely. The fish flavour was most appetising, making her realise that they had eaten very little that day and she had a very real hunger. 'How many servants have you got?' Seeing the young girl Amber realised that she was not as alone in this house as she had at first thought.

'Five altogether,' replied Hamed. 'Mustapha, my cook, also does the housekeeping, Fatima, whom you have just seen, and her sister Hayat. They will look after your every need. There is a bell in your room which will summon either one of them day or night. Then there is my gardener, Rached, and of course Mohammed, who is what you might term a general dogsbody.'

'All these people just to look after you?' asked Amber, sceptically lifting her fine brows. 'Isn't it rather pretentious?'

'Are you suggesting I do the housework myself,' a frown darkened Hamed's brow, 'as well as run my estate and attend to the ever-increasing pile of paper-work?'

Rafika too put in a word in Hamed's defence. 'Don't you realise what a busy man he is? Has Hamed not told you all about his olive groves? They are the finest in the country.'

'I didn't know,' said Amber hesitantly.

'But you knew he was rich,' came back Rafika quickly.

'He would have to be, living in a place like this,' returned Amber, 'but he's told me nothing of his work.'

'Yet you agreed to marry him without knowing anything of his background.' Rafika looked from Amber to the man at her side. 'Is this some kind of joke, Hamed? Why did you not tell Amber? Who knows, she might not like to be a *farmer*'s wife. Does she know exactly what she is letting herself in for? Perhaps I ought to have a quiet word with her, put her completely in the picture.'

'I think, Rafika,' answered Hamed coldly, 'that it might pay you to mind your own business. What I choose to tell Amber is up to me.'

But Rafika appeared not to notice the warning tone in his voice. 'You mean,' she continued, 'that you intended Amber to fall for you for yourself alone and not what your name stands for?' Her lip curled scornfully. 'I doubt she would be so naïve. One only has to look at you to see that you're wealthy. I think maybe it is you, Hamed, who should be careful.'

'If you think that I've been running after your— your friend——' interjected Amber hotly, 'you're mistaken. Hamed has done nothing but——'

'That is enough—both of you.' Hamed put down his spoon and stood up. 'Please remember that Amber is a guest in my house, Rafika, and I will not have her insulted. If you cannot be civil I suggest you leave. And you, Amber, I'm disappointed that you should rise to Rafika's bait. I know she is jealous of you and does not care what she says, but I would like you to be friends. There will be occasions when I am out of the house and Rafika could be good company. I am sure she will be delighted to oblige, if only to please me?' He turned a winning smile on the young girl who, after scowling for a few seconds, visibly relaxed.

'When you ask me like that how can I refuse? You know I will do anything for you, Hamed. Perhaps it might be a good idea if I bring a few clothes and stay for a while?'

So that she could keep an eye on what was going on between the two of them, thought Amber, and was relieved when Hamed shook his head. Not that she wanted to be alone with him, she hastened to assure herself, but the thought of this resentful girl being continually present was even more abhorrent.

'I do not think that will be necessary. There will be occasions when Amber and I wish to be alone and I am sure you would not care to be *de trop*?' He sat down and picked up his spoon once again. 'Shall we continue with our meal? Mustapha will be most disappointed if we do not do it justice.'

Rafika was quiet after that, picking at her food, a petulant expression revealing her innermost thoughts. Hamed ignored her, turning his full attention upon Amber.

Silently and discreetly Fatima took away their dishes and brought in the main course. '*Couscous*,' pronounced Hamed, seeing Amber's questioning look. 'Mustapha thought you would like to try one of our national dishes.'

Amber had heard that it was made from semolina and was relieved to find that it looked nothing like her memories of school pudding. The semolina, Hamed informed her, was moistened with water and oil and then cooked in a special colander over boiling meat or vegetables, from which it extracted some of its flavour

Afterwards it was flavoured with *harissa*, a spice made from dried red pepper, salt and garlic.

The *couscous* was accompanied by pieces of meat and vegetables and Amber found the whole meal delightful. 'I must meet your chef,' she said, 'and compliment him on his cooking. That was perfectly delicious.'

To follow came almond *bouza*, a sort of custard sprinkled with nuts, and finally thick Turkish coffee, piping hot.

At the end of their meal they moved into the room which Amber had first seen, relaxing on the soft cushions on the floor. They chatted for about an hour, Rafika having forgotten her ill humour and making some effort to be friendly. Soon, though, Hamed suggested she leave. 'If you are late getting home your parents will be worried. I will phone for a taxi.'

'They know I am with you,' she argued. 'Ring them and then I can stay as long as I like.'

'But I don't want you here,' he insisted goodhumouredly. 'Can't you see that I want to be alone with Amber?'

'I suppose you will always be sending me away now that she's here,' said Rafika spitefully. 'It never used to be like that. You always said you enjoyed my company.'

'So I did, my little one, and I still do, but not now. Do I have to spell it out for you?'

Amber said nothing, but wished Hamed had not been so insistent that Rafika leave. It meant that until it was time for bed the two of them would be together. As alone as if there were no servants in the house, for she somehow knew that they would not be interrupted.

At the Sahara Beach now her friends would be

puzzling over her absence. Would they make enquiries, she wondered, or guess that she had gone out with Hamed Slouma and not worry at all? There seemed little she could do except take matters as they came and hope that in some way the situation would resolve itself. Hamed could not make her marry him, she was convinced of that, but it was what else he would try to do that worried her. He had said that she was now his property to do with as he liked. If there had been a lock on her bedroom door she would have gone there now while he was saying goodbye to Rafika, but there was no point when he could so easily follow. She could only hope that his intentions were honourable.

When he returned to the room Amber's nerves were stretched to breaking point and while he was filling two glasses at the drinks cabinet she stood up, leaning back against the wall, her fingertips restlessly moving across the painted surface, her breathing erratic and a fearful expression on her face.

When he turned and saw her his face hardened, his easy smile disappearing. 'What the devil's the matter? You look as though you're scared half out of your mind!'

Amber swallowed convulsively, her mouth dry and her heart pumping wildly. 'I—I—nothing. Nothing's the matter. Why should it be?'

He snorted angrily. 'You expect me to believe that when you're pressed back against that wall like a frightened rabbit? I'm not going to rape you, my dear Amber, if that's what you have in mind. I want our association to hold nothing but pleasant memories. Sit down and take your drink. I got rid of Rafika so that you and I could spend a happy evening together. I hope you're not going to deny me that pleasure.'

'Only if you p-promise not to touch me,' said Amber tremulously. Not that she did not want him to, but how could she trust herself? And where would it lead? She was not so sure it would be as innocent as he had intimated.

At her words he slammed down the glasses on one of the low tables, half spilling the contents. 'What is this? You were not averse to my touch a short while ago.' And with sudden intuition, 'Is it yourself you're afraid of—and not me?'

Amber shook her head vigorously, but could not disguise the flicker of truth that shone for one moment in her eyes. 'Of course not. I've told you before that you mean nothing to me.'

'Maybe not—not yet,' he answered mildly, his narrowed eyes watchful, 'but I disturb you, and that is what frightens you. It is written clearly in your eyes.'

Determined to deny all existence of these treacherous feelings, Amber said hotly, 'Oh, go to the devil! I know what type of man you are. You've dragged me here against my will and now that your servants have finished and Rafika gone you think you can get your own way, but if you so much as lay one finger on me I shall scream and scream until someone arrives. Now that I know I'm no longer entirely alone in this house you won't find me so easily swayed by your amorous advances.'

To her surprise he argued no more, sitting down and picking up his glass, sipping the liquid as his eyes ran insolently over her body.

'Do you have to look at me like that?' she snapped, when her nerves could stand no more.

'I like the kaftan,' he remarked agreeably. 'It moulds your curves sufficiently to whet a man's appetite.'

Amber flushed and said, 'I shouldn't let yourself get carried away.'

'I have no intention of doing that,' he replied calmly. 'Unlike you, my passionate one, I have no difficulty in controlling my feelings.'

'How dare you!' Amber stepped forward, her eyes blazing. 'How dare you suggest that I have no self-restraint!'

'Well, have you?' he mocked.

She stared belligerently back. 'I'm always in complete command.'

Thick brows rose in disbelief, but he said, 'I'm glad to hear it.'

'Then you'd better not forget,' she finished crossly.

'Oh, I shan't, but you can rest assured that should your control—perhaps slip—I shall not hesitate to take advantage. I mean, if you're as strong-willed as you say, and then I find you returning my kisses, what am I expected to believe?'

Amber tossed her head. 'You're despicable!'

'And you're beautiful. When you're angry I want to kiss you.'

'Then I must remember never to get angry.' She held her head high and walked towards the door. 'If you'll excuse me I will go to my room. It's been quite a day one way and another and I'm exhausted.'

Unfortunately she had to cross near to Hamed to reach the door. Quick as lightning his arm shot out and he caught her wrist, pulling her down on to the cushion beside him with an ignominious bump. Her loose skirt rode high, showing an embarrassing length of leg, and in an endeavour to tug it down Amber lost her balance altogether. 'You beast, I hate you!' she cried from her position flat on her back.

'Have you not heard that hate is another form of love?' he queried softly, leaning over her and pinning her shoulders to the floor with his large capable hands. 'Your testing time has come sooner than you thought. Are you ready, Amber? Ready to deny the clamouring of your pulses and erratic beating of your heart?' He placed one hand beneath her breast, pausing, his head tilted to one side. 'Ah, already it is beating twice as fast.'

Amber glared, 'Don't flatter yourself! It's only because I was struggling to get up.'

'And the colour in your cheeks? Surely you're not going to disappoint me by saying that it is not due to my nearness?'

'You're so conceited!' she spat through clenched teeth. 'I wish I was a man so that I could fight you, knock some of that egotism out of you.'

'I certainly don't wish you to be a man,' he smiled irritatingly, 'but if you want to fight, go ahead, it could be fun.'

He was displaying that superb self-control that disturbed her. 'What's the point?' she questioned hotly. 'I would only make a fool of myself. Why don't you just let me go? I can't see what enjoyment you get by keeping me here.'

'On the contrary, I'm enjoying myself tremendously. You're very entertaining, Amber, or didn't you know that? You rise to my bait beautifully.'

For a few seconds there was silence while she digested his words. Then she said, with as much dignity as she could muster, 'I didn't realise I was here to amuse you. I thought it was a—wife you wanted.'

'Primarily,' he conceded, 'but this byplay is an added bonus. Of course, it can only lead to one thing, as you well know.' He moved his hand to cover her breast and Amber caught in her breath quickly as her instantly heightened emotions threatened to choke her.

'I know this doesn't mean a thing to you,' she said, as his fingers probed and teased, sliding into the open front of her dress, feeling warm against the soft smoothness of her skin. 'But try to enjoy it. You'll find it infinitely more rewarding than struggling.'

As he lowered his face she closed her eyes, not wanting to see his naked desire. When his mouth found hers it was as though an explosion took place inside her, burning a trail of fire through her limbs, weakening her defences, totally destroying the immunity she had built up.

Despite these feelings she frenziedly tried to push him away, but the more she struggled the harder his kisses became, totally ravaging her senses and demanding surrender.

'No, no!' she mouthed, shaking her head from side to side as his mouth slid down her throat, nudging away the thin material from her shoulders and exposing the creamy fullness of her breasts.

'My darling,' he whispered hoarsely, 'how can I resist such beauty?' For a few seconds he looked down on her nakedness before with a groan he lowered himself on top of her and it was impossible for Amber to ignore the urgency of his body.

With sudden shame she knew that she wanted him, that should he carry their lovemaking to its ultimate end she would be powerless to stop him; indeed even now her hands crept seemingly of their own volition to the hollow of his back, pulling him against her, her lips parted and her breathing ragged and uneven. The last time this had happened she had had the power to stop him, but now it was as though all sanity had departed. Every nerve-end responded, every fibre of her being was vibrantly alive and the blood pounded in her head. She was no longer responsible for her actions.

'Dearest Amber, I am going to make love to you—do you mind?'

His voice reached her as from a distance and she shook her head shamelessly. 'I—I want you to. Oh, Hamed, *I want you.*' Through tear-blurred eyes she looked at him. He had won, but what did it matter? What could possibly matter compared to the whole host of emotions that had taken over her body?

Gently now his fingers traced the outline of her face, stroking away the tears. 'Do you love me, Amber? Do you mind very much?'

She looked up into the depths of his stormy dark eyes, raising one hand to touch the thick curling hair. 'I want what you want,' she whispered, 'and if what I'm feeling right now is love, then yes, I do love you, very much.'

He groaned as he pulled her close once again, but there was a subtle change in his voice when he said, 'That is all I wanted to hear.' And when she looked at him his face had changed. It was as though a mask had been pulled over his feelings. He smiled coolly and sprang to his feet. 'That was all I wanted, dearest Amber. You have lost your battle. The truth has come out. You may go to bed now.'

For a few long tortured seconds Amber lay there, hardly able to comprehend what was happening. Her body clamoured for his touch, but he stood over her with no trace of the deep emotion she was so sure had tempered his actions. It had all been a game, a game designed to force an admission of her feelings—and she had fallen for it! How gullible she had been, and what a fool she felt now.

'Get out!' she shouted. 'Leave me alone. Don't touch me again—*ever!*'

CHAPTEP SIX

THERE had been no sign of Hamed when Amber made her way to her room a few minutes after the scene that had robbed her of every shred of pride. She had flung herself down on the bed asking herself repeatedly why she had fallen for this man who could play about with her feelings with no compunction whatsoever.

There was no doubt in her own mind now that she did love him. She tried to persuade herself that it was flattery, but would that account for the weakness of her body whenever he touched her—or her own breathlessness when she so much as looked at him? Or pure animal magnetism? But even this she discarded, for the thought of returning to England and spending the rest of her life apart from Hamed was suddenly frightening. It had to be love—but this made his rejection of her doubly hard to bear. Though she knew it was only a game he had played it hurt; even the death of her mother had not left this unbearable emptiness inside.

She wanted to run away but was trapped by the love that was growing hourly. Surely there was something she could do? Some way she could remain without losing her dignity altogether? Hamed would expect her now to want to leave, and would take an even greater delight in holding her prisoner—but if there was some other reason for her being here? Perhaps—an idea occurred to her—perhaps she could help him with his paper work? Hadn't he complained about it piling up —and she herself was used to office routine, so it shouldn't be difficult. It would lighten his own load and she would find it fun sharing things with Hamed, becoming an integral part of his life, without feeling that she was being kept here against her will.

She smiled, everything else forgotten. She would tell Hamed of her decision, now. But downstairs all was quiet and dark. He too had gone to bed. Disappointing, but there was nothing she could do except wait until morning.

She slept restlessly, eager to see Hamed, rising as soon as the sun had pushed away the shadow of night. She showered and dressed in a dusky pink trouser suit, unable to dispel the excitement of having a whole new wardrobe of clothes from which to choose. Hamed must think a great deal of her to go to this trouble, and although at the beginning she had resented it she now felt a pleasurable warmth that he had devoted so much care to her well-being.

At this early hour she expected to find the dining room empty and had been prepared to wait for both her breakfast and Hamed. It was a surprise to find Fatima laying the table in readiness.

The young girl looked disconcerted when Amber entered the room. 'I am sorry,' she said in hesitating English, 'breakfast is not yet ready. You are early. We did not expect you down so soon.'

Amber smiled, trying to put Fatima at her ease. 'Don't worry, it's my own fault. I—I couldn't sleep. I'll take a walk in the garden. If Hamed—Mr Slouma —should come down will you tell him where I am?'

Fatima nodded and with a sudden shy smile said, 'It

is nice to have you here, miss. I hope you will be very happy.'

'Thank you, Fatima,' returned Amber, wondering exactly what interpretation the servants had put on her presence. 'Tell me,' she added impulsively, 'has Hamed had many girl-friends staying here?'

Fatima's luminous eyes darted past Amber to some point behind her head before she said, 'I am sorry, miss, I am not at liberty to discuss my employer's private life. If you will excuse me I must get on with my work,' and she scurried from the room as though for some reason she had been afraid to answer. Which was ridiculous, thought Amber, as she only wanted to know the truth.

A sound behind her caused her to spin round. 'Oh, Hamed, how long have you been there?' But even without his answer she knew he had heard her conversation and judging by the frown darkening his brow he was not very pleased.

'If you want to know anything at all about my movements I suggest you ask me, not my servants,' he said brusquely.

'Knowing full well that you wouldn't tell me?' she responded.

'Probably not, if I thought it none of your business, but I do object to you talking about me behind my back and I shall not expect you to do it again. Is that clear?' and when Amber stubbornly refused to answer, 'If you do, I shall find out. My staff respect me and are loyal, so please bear that in mind next time you feel like prying.'

Amber's earlier blissful feeling was crumbling quickly and disappointment added an edge to her voice. 'It's your own reserve that instigated my curiosity. Why was it that I had to find out from Rafika what you did for a living? Why didn't you tell me yourself? You expect to marry me, yet it's you yourself who puts up the barriers.'

With exasperating calm he shrugged and folded his arms across his broad chest. His light cotton shirt strained against his powerful muscles. 'All right. What do you want to know?'

Put baldly like that what did it matter? Her questions would sound petty, especially when there was something so much more important that she wanted to tell him. With an apologetic smile she said, 'I suppose it really doesn't matter. Besides, Hamed, I've been thinking—about us—I——'

'To me it does,' cut in Hamed abruptly. 'If you were so curious a few moments ago you cannot thrust it from your mind. It will only continue to bother you. Now, what was the question, how many girl-friends have I entertained here?' Judging by his smile and the glint in his eye he found the thoughts pleasurable.

'Oh, please,' begged Amber, feeling suddenly uncomfortable, 'I'm not interested, it was a silly question. I—I'm sorry.' After all, what did it matter? Whatever he had done in the past was irrelevant.

But Hamed spoke almost as though he had not heard her protest. 'Douja was the first one, pretty little Douja.' His eyes clouded reminiscently. 'We spent a lot of time together. She was—beautiful.'

The way he hesitated made Amber think that he had been going to say something else. She only had to look at his face to see that his memories of Douja were extremely happy ones, and the thought was displeasing.

'And then came Fatouma. She too was——' He described her shape with his hands. 'Oh, and I mustn't forget Elizabeth.'

'Elizabeth?' asked Amber incredulously. 'Was she English?'

He nodded. 'She was a little like you, fair, pretty, about your age.'

'And did you ask *her* to marry you?' asked Amber in sudden outrage.

'Would it bother you if I had?' His brows slid up expressively as he waited for her reply.

'Let's say I have no wish to be one of a string of girls you've asked to marry you, all of whom have obviously said no. Was that why you *told* me I was going to marry you, instead of asking? Were you afraid of yet another refusal?' Amber felt strangely near to tears. Things were going all wrong. Her good intentions were being overriden before she had even had time to voice them.

'Poor Amber, you really are getting yourself worked up over nothing——'

'Nothing?' she flashed. 'Nothing, when you've just taken great delight in parading your past conquests before me?'

'But only because you asked,' he protested with an innocence she could only believe was assumed.

'I didn't ask *you*. For some reason only known to yourself you insisted on telling me. Were you trying to make me jealous? Is that it?' If so, he had succeeded beyond his wildest dreams, but she would die rather than admit it.

'How could I do that?' he asked. 'You've told me I mean nothing to you, so I assumed that your interest was genuine. I'm sorry if it's caused you distress, that was the farthest thought from my mind.'

Amber stepped back away from his outstretched hand, her chin tilted haughtily. 'It doesn't matter, not in the least, what you've done. I couldn't care less.'

He nodded and gave a satisfied smile. 'Good, that is as it should be,' and with a sudden change of conversation, 'Would you care for a swim before breakfast? I usually do, when I have time.'

'I don't think so,' replied Amber. Their talk had disturbed her deeply and was sufficient to put her off the idea of further intimacies. 'My swimsuit is at the hotel,' she finished lamely, realising he was waiting for a plausible excuse.

'Perhaps you are forgetting I have fully equipped your wardrobe. You will find several bikinis from which to make your choice. Hurry along, Amber, I dislike being kept waiting.' His tone had changed abruptly, brooking no refusal.

Amber turned meekly, wondering why she acted this way instead of sticking up for herself. Did Hamed always get what he wanted? Was she conforming to pattern? By the time she had reached her room she had worked herself up into an outrage. How dared he dictate to her! What right had he to say what she should or should not do? She was a free agent and could make up her own mind. 'No, I will not go swimming,' she said aloud. 'I will not allow him to order me about!' She sat on the edge of the bed, remaining there stubbornly until the sound of footsteps outside warned her that Hamed was coming to see where she was.

She rose and stood facing the door as it opened without even so much as a knock. 'Why aren't you ready?' he asked tersely.

'Because I've changed my mind,' responded Amber with assumed calmness. 'I don't feel like swimming.'

'You don't feel like it,' he repeated slowly. 'What a pity, because you're going. I want your company, and you should know by now that I always get what I want.'

'Then you'll have to drag me there,' retorted Amber, 'because I refuse to move.'

'I will do just that,' he said. 'Do not think I won't, but it would be a pity to spoil your new clothes. First of all I will undress you and put on your bikini.' He strode to the wardrobe and pulled out a brief black and white spotted nylon affair that looked as though it would reveal more than it would cover.

Amber stood her ground, not really believing that he would go so far as to touch her. He was trying to frighten her into obeying him. He was in for a surprise!

But she had misjudged him. With one swift movement he was in front of her, his big hands undoing the buttons on her tunic almost before she had time to stop him. It slid from her shoulders as she fought him and she crossed her arms in an endeavour to cover her body.

'Do not worry,' he grinned, 'I shall see much more of you in this. Do you want me to finish the job or are you ready to carry on yourself?'

'I don't suppose I shall get any peace unless I do!' she flamed. 'But only if you wait outside.'

She half expected him to refuse and was pleasantly surprised when he left. The bikini was nothing more than a few triangles held together by thin straps, and although she felt half naked Amber knew that it showed off her curves to perfection. In the wardrobe she found a towelling robe which she slung about her shoulders before making her way outside.

Hamed, who had been leaning nonchalantly against the wall, turned and led the way along the corridor. The pool was reached by a series of steps at the back of the house and through a covered white archway. Its turquoise-tiled oval looked inviting with the sun sparkling on the softly rippling water. Surrounding the pool were tubs of brilliant flowering shrubs and the ever-present palms, beneath which stood several wooden-framed sun-loungers painted in bright paint-box colours.

Unselfconsciously Hamed stripped off his shirt and slacks beneath which he wore a pair of tan swimming trunks almost the same colour as his skin. 'Are you ready?' he asked Amber as she stood poised on the edge of the pool. She had discarded the robe beside his clothes and had waited for his comments on the minuscule bikini. When he gave her no more than a cursory glance she felt disappointed. Quite what she had expected she did not know, but certainly more than this apparent total lack of interest.

In answer to his question she dived cleanly into the pool, gasping at the coldness of the water and surfacing to find him close by her side. 'I thought you said it was heated,' she said, shivering in its icy depths.

'It's not working at the moment,' he grinned. 'Come on, you'll soon get warm. We'll have a race—three lengths. The winner decides what we shall do today.'

'That's not fair,' she retorted, 'you know full well you'll win.'

'Okay, you do two lengths. I'll start from the other end.'

Amber watched the effortless ease with which he cut through the water. She doubted whether she would beat him, even with one length start, but somehow it became important that she did. If she could dictate their movements today it would throw open a whole world of ideas. She could even insist that he take her back to the Sahara Beach, and knowing instinctively that he was a man of his word how could he refuse? Last night she had not wanted to leave, but after his revelations this morning there seemed little point in staying. Who wanted to be one of many? He had not actually said he had asked anyone else to marry him, but he had not denied it either. And then there was Rafika. Where did she figure in his plans? Admittedly she was young, but she was every inch a woman and knew what she wanted—even if Hamed himself was sublimely unaware of it. And that type of woman normally got her own way.

'Right,' shouted Hamed, cutting into her thoughts. 'Go!'

They began their respective lengths, passing each other before Amber had covered half of the first one. Hamed grinned and gave her a mock salute as he continued his easy powerful strokes.

It was on her second length that the muscles in Amber's legs contracted painfully, making it impossible for her to carry on. The pool was deep at this point and she floundered helplessly for a few seconds before calling out, 'Hamed, help me, I've got cramp!'

At first he thought she was pretending and was after an excuse to stop the race. But when he realised that she really was in trouble he was by her side instantly. His hands beneath her shoulders, he swam with her to the edge of the pool, lifting her effortlessly up in his arms and laying her down on the edge where he proceeded to massage the knotted muscles in her legs.

To begin with the pain was so great that Amber lay there, her eyes closed, allowing him to minister to her needs, but as the pain eased there came an awareness. This was the man she loved, but she would not tell him so again—not after this morning. He was a Casanova, she decided, and although his offer of marriage had seemed genuine she had no proof that he would go through with it. For all she knew he only wanted to get her into bed and afterwards would discard her with as little compunction as when he had told Rafika to go the previous evening.

She kept her eyes closed so that he should not read her innermost thoughts. His firm hands on her legs sent quivers of emotion through her limbs and she longed to pull that handsome brown head close and feel his mouth against her. Without realising it her lips parted and the tip of her moist pink tongue ran over them. Hamed's hands travelled up the length of her thighs and Amber's eyes shot open, but there was nothing in his face to suggest that his motives had been anything other than honourable. 'I think that's it,' he said, pushing himself to his feet. 'Time we went in for breakfast.' He held out his hand and hesitantly she put her own into it, allowing him to pull her up. She was cold but could feel the warmth radiating from

Hamed as for one second they stood so close they were almost touching. Droplets of water still clung to the dark hairs on his chest and beneath his mahogany skin muscles rippled, suggesting that he did much of the hard work on the estate himself. For one heartstopping second she thought he was going to pull her into his arms. His dark eyes narrowed fractionally as they rested upon her face, but the next moment the expression had gone and he let her go, picking up her robe and draping it carelessly about her shoulders.

He strode ahead of her towards the house and was soon lost to sight beneath the curved archway. He had not bothered to put on his shoes and a trail of damp footprints on the tiled floor told her clearly which way he had gone. They stopped at a door opposite to her own and she frowned. She had not realised that he slept so close. She was still standing debating on the situation when his door was yanked open and he came out, stopping abruptly when he saw her standing outside.

'Why aren't you ready?' he asked, almost coldly. It had taken him no more than a few seconds to towel himself dry and change into a pair of fawn slacks and short-sleeved matching shirt. His damp hair was combed close to his head but already unruly curls were springing back into life.

'I—I——' she began, not really knowing what to say. 'I'm just going,' and she hurried into her room before he could say anything more. His attitude puzzled her. It was as though after last night, when she had admitted her love, he had lost all interest. He had not so much as attempted to kiss her this morning, which was not like the Hamed she knew. A frown creased her brow as she took a quick dip under the warming shower before dressing once more in the pink trouser suit.

Over breakfast Hamed told her that something had cropped up on the estate and that he would have to leave her to her own devices. 'I shall try not to be long,' he said, 'but one never knows, and in case I am late I have arranged for Rafika to spend the day here so that you will not be lonely.'

'I don't like Rafika,' said Amber instantly before she could stop herself, but not really caring now whether she upset Hamed or not. Rafika was his friend, not hers, so her opinion of the young girl could in no way matter. 'I shall be perfectly all right by myself—or don't you trust me—is that it?' Quick anger that he should think it necessary to provide her with an escort built up. 'Do you think I might try to run away?'

'The thought had occurred to me,' he returned mildly, 'but I hope you will not be so foolish.'

'Foolish?' echoed Amber. 'It's hardly the word I would use. Brave is more like it.'

'It is a pity you regard yourself as a prisoner here,' he said, putting down his knife with which he had been buttering his roll, 'for that is not what I intended. I want you to be happy, Amber. In a few days we will be married. Why not spend the time getting used to the idea and preparing yourself for——'

'For what?' broke in Amber icily, 'for sharing your bed? Do you really expect me to believe that you'll wait until it's all legal? If you wanted to take me you would, don't bother to deny it. It puzzles me why you——' She stopped abruptly, not wishing to put into words her humiliation of the previous evening.

But Hamed with his keen perception knew exactly what was going on in her mind. 'Why I left you feeling frustrated last night?' His eyes glinted wickedly. 'Perhaps your desires were greater than mine, or do you think it could be that I have more self-control? You're very transparent, my charming one. I always know exactly what is going on in that head of yours.' He took a bite from his crusty roll and studied her calmly. 'For instance, I know that you are eaten up with curiosity as to why my feelings towards you have apparently changed.'

Amber swallowed hastily and looked down at her plate. Was she really so obvious?

'Perhaps it will put your mind at rest if I explain that I think it only fair to give you time to come to terms with yourself. Perhaps I am rushing you too much. I should hate to have a hostile bride on my wedding day.'

She could not make up her mind whether Hamed was serious or not. He sounded it, but surely he did not intend to go through with this ludicrous idea of marrying her. She said as much, noting his frown of impatience at what he clearly considered a pointless question.

'I have never been more serious in my life.' An arrogant tilt to his head added emphasis to his reply. 'That is one thing you had better make clear in your mind. You are going to be my wife and nothing or no one will stand in my way.'

'Despite the fact that you don't love me?' flung back Amber uncaringly. 'What sort of a marriage do you think it will be? Oh, I wish I understood you. I wish I knew what this farce was all about!'

Hamed wiped his mouth on a napkin and picked up his coffee cup. 'One day you will learn the truth. Until then I suggest you try to control that temper of yours and take each day as it comes. Tunisia is a beautiful place and I pride myself on my home. Enjoy it, Amber. You only have one life, why spoil it with harsh thoughts?'

'Have you ever not known where you were going, Hamed? Have you ever felt so uncertain of the future that it terrifies you?' Amber disregarded the warning glint in his eye. 'No, of course you haven't. You have your own fine home and your servants, everything that money can buy. But it won't buy me. You think you're a little god sitting in your palace, lifting your finger for everyone to do your bidding, but this is one girl who can see right through you, and you'll never get your way with me, not if you keep me here until I'm a hundred!'

For one moment she thought she had gone too far. Hamed had risen, his tightened jaw and dark narrowed eyes clear evidence that he too was angry. When he curled one hand into a fist she thought he was surely going to hit her and closed her eyes, tensing herself for the inevitable. After a few long seconds, when nothing happened, she squinted through her lashes, still sure that some terrible punishment was about to come her way. But the room was empty. With that superb self-control of his he had curbed his temper and left her to finish her breakfast alone.

She scraped back her chair and stood up, only then realising that her limbs were trembling. She had got away lightly, she realised that, but did not regret any-

thing she said. She had meant every word. He was
lord and master of his estate, a respected man in the
area, according to Rafika, and no doubt used to issuing
orders and having them obeyed. Perhaps Tunisian
girls liked their men masterful, she thought, but she
was English, and proud of it, and if he wanted to
marry her he would have to win her love, and then
ask her, not *command* it. It was like some fictional
tale of which one only read. It just couldn't be happening to her. It was too ludicrous for words.

CHAPTER SEVEN

It truly was beautiful. There was no denying the fact, thought Amber, having completed a further tour of the house and gardens. With Hamed at her side yesterday she had been more aware of the man himself than her surroundings, but now she had spent more than an hour admiring the exquisite Moorish style villa and the vast gardens resplendent with flowering shrubs as well as orange and lemon trees, to say nothing of the pomegranates and bananas. She had picked an orange as she walked and decided that never before had the fruit tasted so sweet.

Now she sat in an inner courtyard, with rooms opening off on all four sides. Above her the sun blazed down and all about her was colour. Purple bougainvillea frothed over a white stone arch and crimson hibiscus beneath it vied for attention. The pale rose hid itself shyly in a corner while the more flamboyant geraniums grew proudly in ornamental tubs. It was a haven of peace and Amber wriggled on her wrought iron chair trying to make herself more comfortable.

The anger she had felt after her outburst had faded. Who could be cross for long amidst such tranquillity? Hamed's way of life was different from hers—perhaps she had been wrong to blame him for his high-handed manner. It came natural to him, whereas she herself had never come up against anyone of his type before. In her office job she had encountered all sorts of

people, but they were all ordinary and had none of the
natural arrogance so typical of Hamed. When she had
left work to look after her mother she had had hardly
any connection at all with the outside world. Doctor
Greer was the only member of the opposite sex with
whom she had come into direct contact. And he was a
dear. She recalled how concerned he had been over her
future and had it not been for his insistence she would
never have come to Tunisia.

She smiled as she wondered what he would think if
he could see her now. She was sure that if he had had
any idea that anything like this would happen he
would not have sent her. It might be a good idea to
write to him. Maybe he could use his influence to get
her away. But she knew she wouldn't. Hamed's house
was beginning to ensnare her, perhaps more so than the
man himself.

A few minutes later her reverie was rudely interrupted. 'So there you are! I've been looking all over
for you.' It was Rafika, dressed in a smart woollen
suit in vibrant green, looking as though she had
stepped straight out of a Paris magazine. Amber at
first thought her overdressed before she realised that
this was the beginning of the Tunisian winter and
although she herself found it warm the inhabitants
thought it distinctly chilly. She recalled seeing some
of the men in Sousse dressed in thick winter overcoats
while she herself had worn nothing more than a sun-
dress.

'Oh, hello, Rafika,' she said. 'Hamed really need not
have bothered you. I enjoy my own company.'

'It will give us an opportunity to talk,' said Rafika
silkily, pulling up a chair beside her. 'I think there

is much you need to know about Hamed and me.'

'I doubt it. I can't see that your private lives are any concern of mine.'

The dark oval eyes looked steadily at Amber. 'They are when it concerns my happiness. I think you are maybe under a misapprehension.'

Amber frowned. 'I'm sorry, I don't understand.'

'Hamed introduced you as his fiancée. From that I take it he has asked you to marry him?' Rafika paused expectantly.

Amber said, 'And if he has?'

'He is making a fool of you. Nothing will ever come of it.'

Disliking the vehement tone of the other girl's voice, Amber said, 'What makes you so sure?'

Rafika studied her well-manicured nails. 'Hamed and I have known each other all our lives and there has been an understanding between our two families that we would one day get married.'

Amber frowned. 'I did not know that arranged marriages still took place here?' She struggled to keep her composure and not let Rafika know how disturbed she was by this information. She was sure Hamed did not love Rafika, as sure as she was that he did not love her. She had seen the way he treated the younger girl, more like a little sister than anything else. There had certainly been nothing loverlike in his attentions.

'Oh, yes, in certain families,' returned Rafika haughtily.

'But Hamed has no family, so surely he has a right to speak for himself.'

Rafika's beautiful eyes narrowed. 'It was what his parents wanted before they died and if you know

Hamed as well as I do you would know that he will respect their wishes.'

Amber was not convinced. 'If that is so why has he not married you before now?'

'He is——' Rafika shrugged, 'he is waiting for me to—well, he said I am too young,' she finished defensively.

'You mean you have discussed marriage?'

'Of course.' Rafika's chin jutted.

'Or would I be right in thinking that it is you who have asked him, not the other way round?' asked Amber. Rafika had suddenly become uneasy, confirming Amber's suspicion that it had all been a bluff. 'I haven't known Hamed long, but I don't think he's the type of man who would two-time anyone.'

'Two-time? What is that?' asked Rafika crossly.

'I mean,' exclaimed Amber impatiently, 'that he wouldn't ask me to marry him knowing full well that he was committed to you.'

Rafika stood up and turned her back. 'He asks many girls to marry him. It means nothing.' She turned abruptly. 'But *I* am the one he loves. I know and understand Hamed. I love him——' her voice broke, 'and soon, when he realises that I am a child no more, I will show him that Rafika knows how to love.'

Amber suddenly felt sorry for her. Unless she was badly mistaken Rafika was harbouring a delusion. It was true she loved Hamed, or thought she did, having grown up at his side and worshipped him all these years. But as for Hamed returning her feelings, Amber very much doubted it. He was at least twice the girl's age and from the short time she had seen them together Amber was sure his feelings went no deeper than pure friendship. 'It wouldn't be wise to build up your hopes too much,' she said kindly. 'You could be wrong. Hamed——'

'Are you jealous?' snapped Rafika, without waiting for her to finish. 'Can't you bear the thought that he might prefer me instead of you? Well, let me tell you something else, you are not the first girl he has brought home, nor do I expect you will be the last.'

'Yes, I know. Hamed told me.'

This information shocked Rafika, her eyes widening into huge twin orbs. 'You are lying,' she cried desperately. 'Why should he boast about it?'

'Because I asked him,' replied Amber. 'I couldn't believe I was the only girl in whom he'd been interested. A man as attractive as Hamed must have had countless affairs.'

'And you are not bothered?' Rafika was clearly unable to believe that Amber was as indifferent as she made out.

'It's in the past,' shrugged Amber. 'It's the present that's all-important.' She found it easy to put on a face in front of the younger girl. 'You'll find that out as you get older.'

Rafika glared. 'Don't you start! I have enough with Hamed treating me as though I am still a schoolgirl!'

Mercifully at that moment Fatima brought out a tray of mint tea and the two girls sat in silence for a few minutes; Rafika brooding over her period of adolescence while Amber herself wondered what they were going to do for the rest of the day. With Rafika in this mood it did not augur well for the time at their disposal. Had the young girl been well disposed towards her they could have spent a few pleasant hours

swimming and sunbathing. Then she remembered that
the water would be too cold for Rafika. If she wanted
to swim it would have to be alone, and after her painful experience that morning she deemed it wise not
to go in again. What then could they do? She was
about to ask whether she had any preference when
Rafika spoke, indicating all too clearly what was on
her mind:

'If Hamed does not marry me he will still not marry
you. I have seen it happen too often to believe that he
is serious this time. He has some sort of notion that it
flatters a girl if he asks her to marry him, but he never
keeps his promise.'

Amber forced a smile. 'Are you warning me or
threatening me? I'm perfectly capable of judging
Hamed's sincerity for myself.'

'And you think he is sincere?' Rafika's doubt was
reflected in her clear brown eyes.

The truth was Amber did not. She had mistrusted
Hamed right from the beginning, still not sure what
game he was playing, but she would not give Rafika
the pleasure of knowing this. 'I have no reason to
doubt him,' she said with conviction.

'Not after what I've told you?'

Amber shrugged. 'I knew most of it and guessed
the rest. It came as no surprise.'

Rafika rose, brushing against the tray carelessly and
apparently deliberately, knocking the delicate china
cups on to the stone floor so that they smashed into
irreparable pieces. 'I'm wasting my time here. I don't
know why I bothered to come,' and disregarding the
damage she rushed back into the house.

Amber dropped to her knees and began picking up

the tiny pieces, distressed to see such beautiful cups destroyed, exclaiming aloud as a needle-sharp fragment dug into her finger and realising the folly of trying to gather up the pieces by hand. The wisest thing would be to find Fatima and ask for a dustpan and brush.

On his tour of the house Hamed had not shown her the kitchens, stating firmly that she would never need to use them. 'I pay my staff well,' he had added, 'they will look after your every need.'

But Amber was not used to giving orders and did not like asking Fatima to clear up the mess. Besides, it would find her something to do in what promised to be an interminable day.

She found the kitchens down a flight of steps at the far side of the house. They were modern and clean and something with a tempting aroma was simmering on the stove—but finding a brush was not so easy.

'Just what do you think you are doing?'

Amber brought up her head from a cupboard in which she had been searching, encountering the hard questioning stare of Hamed.

'I find Rafika frantically telephoning for a taxi and you in the kitchen where you have no right. What has gone on between you?' he demanded.

If Rafika had not told him Amber felt that she had no right to betray the other girl, although Hamed would have to be blind if he did not know Rafika loved him. She shrugged carelessly. 'Rafika decided to go home. There was nothing I could do to stop her.'

'I don't suppose you even tried,' he returned shortly. 'And you—what are you doing in here? If there was something you wanted you only had to ring the bell.'

Amber tossed her head. 'I'm not entirely incapable, you know. I'm not used to servants, nor do I think it a good idea to use them when I can do the job myself. If you would tell me where you keep your brushes I can get on with the job I started.'

His frown deepened. 'Brushes? What do you intend doing? No wife of mine will spend her time cleaning.'

The whole thing was growing out of all proportion, but with his deepening anger Amber felt only a stubbornness not to tell him what she really wanted a brush for. Let him think she was going to do some housework! Serve him right for being so pompous! What did he think he was—a lord? 'I'm not afraid of dirtying my hands,' she said pointedly, 'and if you won't tell me where they're kept I'd better go on searching.'

At that moment a heavily built man came into the room. He wore a white nylon coat over his grey trousers and blue shirt. His face was lined and interesting and Amber judged him to be well into his fifties. It had to be Mustapha. Who else would look at her with such obvious annoyance—apart from Hamed, of course, but despite his displeasure his respect for his master was such that he said nothing, merely looking interrogatingly from one to the other.

'Ah, Mustapha,' said Hamed. 'Perhaps you will tell Miss Christy that there is no need for her to do any work. She insists she is after a sweeping brush, though what she intends to do I have no idea.'

The look Mustapha bestowed on Amber made it clear that he thought this a slight on his housekeeping, but in deference to the fact that she was a friend of Hamed's he said politely, 'What was it you intended to do, Miss Christy? If you have any complaints I would rather you told me than attempt to rectify them yourself.'

The situation was now completely out of hand and Amber looked helplessly from one to the other. 'If you must know,' she said with attempted dignity, realising there was no point in hiding the truth any longer, 'all I wanted to do was clear up the mess from a tray that was accidentally knocked over. Surely there's nothing against me doing that little job?'

Had she realised the effect her words would have Amber might have been tempted to keep quiet. Mustapha clapped a hand to his mouth. 'The priceless china! I told Fatima not to use it, but the stupid girl insisted.' He ended in a torrent of Arabic, apparently begging the pardon of Hamed Ben Slouma.

Amber too felt aghast. She had known it was beautiful, but not its value. Now she felt nothing but reproach for Rafika's carelessness. And yet the girl had not bothered, had not even looked down at the shattered remnants. She must have known it was something special. Had she thoughts only for herself, her own pitiful love, so that anything as mundane as a tea-set meant nothing to her?

Judging by the accusing faces now turned upon her it was evident that the two men both thought she had been the one to cause the damage, and Mustapha's distress was so great that one would think that the china had belonged to him. It would be like telling tales now to say that Rafika had done it. They would think she was trying to pass the blame on to the absent girl to clear herself, so Amber said nothing, standing before them feeling something like a prisoner waiting for his sentence.

'You had better go and see, Mustapha,' said Hamed at length. 'Perhaps they can be repaired.'

Amber could have told him that it was no use, but she said nothing, wishing she could just turn and walk out of the kitchen, but realising it would appear nothing short of an admission of guilt. And to say she was sorry would achieve nothing either. How could apologies replace the broken cups? So she stood there, abject misery on her face, her lids lowered so that she could not see the censure in Hamed's eyes.

When Mustapha returned, shaking his head, Hamed said, 'They have been in my family for generations, but you would not know that, Amber. I do not blame you. It is Fatima who was wrong. She must go. I do not wish such another expensive mistake.'

'Oh, no!' exclaimed Amber. 'You can't blame her. She wanted—to impress me, I think. An understandable feeling.'

'Then she should have told you to be careful. Perhaps I ought to warn you now that my house is full of such valuables. Some of them inherited, some collector's pieces. I would appreciate it if you did not touch them.'

'Are you suggesting I'm accident-prone?' asked Amber heatedly, hurt that he should even think such a thing.

'No,' he replied calmly. 'But perhaps you are not accustomed to having rare objects about you. One has to be that little bit more careful than under normal circumstances.'

He spoke patiently, as though she was a child to

whom he had to explain things in great detail. Amber said hotly, 'In that case why do you not put your precious possessions in a glass case where they can't possibly get broken?'

'Because I like them about me,' he said. 'It has never before been necessary to hand out any warnings.'

And it had to be me, thought Amber despondently. She had been brought here against her will and now had to suffer the indignity of being accused of something she had not done. If he thought she was so clumsy why did he not send her away? It would solve his own problems as well as Amber's and it would be best to go now before her love grew too great to bear parting. 'In that case,' she said, deciding she may as well voice her thoughts, 'why don't you take me back to the Sahara Beach? At least then you'll have no need to fear that I'll cause any further damage.'

His dark eyes hardened as he looked into the paler brown of her own. 'If I thought you had deliberately broken that tea-set in order to get sent away—I would——'

He broke off, but Amber knew what he had been going to say. 'You're a sadistic brute!' she yelled. 'Do you really think me capable of such a thing? Why, I never even realised the value of it until a few minutes ago. If you would like me to pay for it—just say so.'

One brow quirked. 'Do you know what you're saying? It would take a lifetime using every penny you earn, and even then you would only pay a fraction of its value. No, it was an unfortunate accident and something best forgotten.' He turned reassuringly to Mustapha, who still looked as worried as if he had broken the china himself. 'Do not blame yourself, my good man. What is done is done. I will talk to Fatima. She will not be so careless again.'

With that he took Amber's elbow and led her from the kitchen. Rafika had disappeared, seemingly unaware of the distress she had left behind. 'I suggest you get yourself ready for lunch,' he said. 'We don't want to upset Mustapha even further by being late.' His voice sounded normal, but there was a closed expression on his face which told Amber that he was not as calm over the incident as he pretended to be.

Fatima did not serve their lunch. Hayat appeared, an almost identical version of the other girl, but she was subdued and Amber guessed that Hamed had already spoken to Fatima who in turn had relayed the conversation to her sister.

When she returned to her room later she found Fatima unpacking her suitcases that had somehow appeared from the Sahara Beach, a trace of recent tears still on her face.

Before Amber could speak she cried out, 'Oh, miss, I am so sorry. It was all my fault. I should never have touched it. But you are so pretty and delicate, like the china, I wanted you to use it—it seemed so right for you—and now look what has happened! The master will never forgive me. Oh, what shall I do?' Her tears started afresh, streaming down the dark cheeks and dropping on to the front of her yellow blouse. She clutched Amber's arm, her wide eyes imploring, all the vulnerability of her youth very much in evidence.

Amber attempted a comforting smile, but she herself felt so miserable that it was an effort. She placed an arm about Fatima's shoulders. 'I'm sure Mr Slouma will not be unreasonable,' she said. 'It's natural he's upset. The cups were one of his showpieces, they are irreplaceable. Did you not know that?'

Fatima shook her head. 'I knew they were pretty, that is all, and I thought why should pretty things not be used. It seemed such a pity for them to stand on that shelf day after day with no one touching them except when they needed washing.'

Had Amber not learned their true value she might have agreed, but now she said, 'It's a hard lesson you have learned today, that we have all learned, I think, but no good will come by worrying. So dry your eyes and try to carry on your duties as you did before.' She crossed to her dressing table and pulled a handkerchief from the drawer, offering it to the sobbing girl. She felt sorry for Fatima, but at the same time the girl had to realise exactly what it was she had done. It was no use being too sympathetic.

Eventually Fatima became calmer. 'I—I suppose I am lucky not to have lost my job,' she said huskily. 'I do not know what I should have done if I had. My mother desperately needs the money. Hayat and I are the oldest of ten and she relies on the money we take home to feed the others.'

'Well, you haven't lost your job,' said Amber matter-of-factly, 'but you'd better pull yourself together and start work, or you'll find yourself in trouble again.'

'Yes, you're right.' Fatima scurried towards the door. 'Thank you for listening. I miss my mother—and I needed someone to talk to.'

Amber had never looked upon herself as a mother figure before, but considering that Fatima could be no more than thirteen or fourteen she supposed that to her she did indeed represent an older woman in whom she could confide. Apart from herself and her sister it was an all-male household—a disturbing enough thought at the best of times. She smiled wryly and changed her sandals for a pair of low-heeled walking shoes. She needed the peace and serenity of the garden. She needed to be alone to gather her chaotic thoughts together.

She was thankful no one saw her go out of the house —she had no desire for Hamed's company. How could she think rationally with him at her side when he was the main reason for her despair?

She paused for a while beside the pool. It seemed an age since this morning when she had lain by its side, Hamed rubbing her leg and sending shivers of passion running through her body. It was strange he had shown no feelings of emotion himself—almost as if he had grown immune to her. He had been the perfect, attentive lover until last night, and now it was as though he had accomplished what he had set out to do and had no further interest. She did not believe his explanation that he was giving her time to come to terms with herself—that was ridiculous.

Was Rafika right? Did he in fact make a habit of proposing to girls, rejecting them once he had won their undying love? It was a curious pastime and she had thought that Rafika was making it up in order to make her, Amber, jealous. But now as memories came tumbling back, she realised that since Hamed had more or less forced that declaration of love out of her he had scarcely paid her any attention at all. The thought hurt, it hurt damnably, and she turned away from the pool, walking swiftly between the palms and cypresses away from the house.

She had not ventured this far before, but now the
dark green of the cypresses gave way to the lighter
green of the citrus and farther still the restful silvery
leaves of the olive. These then were Hamed's olive
groves. For as far as the eye could see were rows upon
rows of trees, casting long sloping lines of shadow,
their silver-grey leaves cool against the yellow sand.
Amber stood for a few moments entranced before walking between the uniform rows. The fruit was already
swelling and ripening, but Hamed had told her that it
would be at least another month before it was ripe
enough to pick. 'And then begins our busy season,' he
had said, 'when everyone for miles around comes to
help pick the fruit.' She wondered whether he would
allow her to help, or whether that too would be considered too menial a task.

Without turning round she suddenly realised that
she was being followed, and it struck her then that
during the twenty-four hours she had been at the villa
she had never once been left alone for any consider-
able length of time. She was unobtrusively being
guarded! She really was a prisoner, a thought sufficiently frightening to make her breath catch in her
throat. Her legs felt rubbery and she leaned back
against one of the trees, her heartbeats quickening
painfully. Just what devious game was Hamed Ben
Slouma playing?

CHAPTER EIGHT

AMBER was not surprised to see that it was Hamed
walking lazily between the rows of trees, his hands
thrust into the pockets of his trousers. He had the
slow, easy movement of a tiger, she observed. He looked
relaxed but was ready to pounce at the slightest pro-
vocation.

'So this is where you are,' he said, halting at her
side and resting one elbow against the bole of the tree.
'Rached said he saw you coming this way. Are you
admiring my olives?' Words lightly spoken but prov-
ing without a shadow of doubt that she was being
watched and was a prisoner as truly as if she had been
behind bars.

'I was resting,' said Amber indifferently, 'but yes, I
suppose they are impressive. You must be very rich to
own all this.'

'And does it bother you?' he asked, a sardonic
gleam lightening his eyes. 'In my experience it is the
one thing guaranteed to attract a woman.'

The lean length of his body was only inches away
from her own and a faint lingering odour of the soap
he used reached her nostrils. It incited her without her
quite knowing why, but she refused to move away
and give him the pleasure of knowing that his nearness
was in any way disturbing. She looked up into the
deep velvet eyes above her own, holding his gaze with
a scarcely perceptible lift of her chin. 'Then perhaps

you've been mixing with the wrong type. If I loved a man I wouldn't care whether he was rich or poor.'

His other arm came round the back of her, imprisoning her against the tree, the whispering leaves closing behind them like a blanket. 'But I thought you loved *me*?' His voice was like a caress, subtly trying to persuade her to tell him the truth. 'Why then do you say, "*if* you loved a man"? There can be no ifs about it. By your own admission, my sweet passion flower, your heart belongs to me and you may as well know now that I have no intention of relinquishing it.'

'I must have been mad,' declared Amber passionately, 'when I said that to you. Why should I love you? Your manner towards me has been far from lover-like ever since that admission.'

'I have had other things on my mind,' he said gently, 'but it distresses me that you should think my intentions are less than honourable.' He took her hand and held it against his chest. 'Feel how strongly beats my heart. It is beating for you, my desirable Amber.'

With his firm powerful body beneath her hand Amber could not quell the quickening of her own heart. The scene was set, she thought. If he took her into his arms now all would be lost. His close proximity had set off some crazy impulse inside her which was blossoming into a full-scale assault on her senses. No matter how much she told herself that he was a villain, that he had some ulterior motive in bringing her here to his villa, she could not deny the intense physical attraction between them. 'Words come easily to you,' she cried bravely. 'Do you really expect me to believe them?'

'I would never knowingly lie,' he said with an aggrieved air.

'Nor would you tell me all the facts. It lies with your friend Rafika to fill me in on the real Hamed Slouma.'

An odd light shone in his eyes. 'Ah, so my little Rafika has been up to her tricks again! No wonder she was in a hurry to get away. What tales, I wonder, has she been spinning this time?'

Amber lifted her fine brows coolly. 'So far as I'm concerned she told me nothing but the truth.'

He inclined his head gravely. 'You are perfectly at liberty to believe her, but I think I should warn you that she has a highly fertile imagination and will stop at nothing to blacken me in the eyes of other females. She has tried it many times before—always, I might add, with success.'

So it was true, thought Amber with surprising despondency. Everything that Rafika had said was true, otherwise why did he not deny it? He must have some sort of idea of the things she had said. She could not believe that he would let his young friend get away with it—not if he truly thought anything of her. Or perhaps it was Rafika he would turn to in the end. She could be right when she said that he was waiting for her to grow up—and meanwhile he spent his time amusing himself with any available girl who took his fancy.

'I can see your thoughts disturb you,' he continued at length, and leaning a fraction closer, 'Do you think I ought to do something to take your mind off such problems?'

The look in his eyes sent a shiver of anticipation through Amber. It was not difficult to read his mind and she lowered her lashes, looking away from those dark, stirring depths, not realising that this very action gave away her uncertainty. 'I—I think I should like to go back to the house,' she said hesitantly.

'When I am ready,' he said with a soft firmness she knew could not be denied. 'It amuses me now to spend a few moments alone with you knowing that we will not be disturbed.'

'So I am your plaything?' returned Amber hotly, 'someone with whom to *amuse* yourself when you have nothing better to do. If that's how you feel you can let me go right now,' and for the first time she struggled to escape.

But all she succeeded in doing was to bring herself closer to Hamed and as their bodies touched his arms came behind her, pinning her to him. 'Surely this is far more pleasurable than spending time on your own,' he murmured, the fingers of one hand caressing her nape and sending shivers of anticipation down her spine.

But quelling these thoughts she said distantly, 'No doubt it is to you, but it sickens me that you think you can dally with my feelings whenever you like.'

'My dearest Amber, I never dally with a woman's feelings. I am always perfectly sincere. Do you really doubt me?'

Enfolded in his arms and with her heart beating an erratic tattoo against her breast, how could she deny it? Every nerve-end clamoured for his touch, his kisses, it was only deep down that she knew the truth. The important thing was, did it matter? Did she care that she might be one of many, discarded as soon as he had finished amusing himself? Or was the experience sufficient to make it all worth while? Was that what she wanted—the tortuous pleasure of Hamed's love now—and then nothing? It came as something of a shock when she realised that this was what she would settle for, making her wonder what type of a person she had become to allow herself to be used by this foreigner with the devastating looks and glib tongue.

She did not speak, but it was as though Hamed had read her thoughts, for he gave a satisfied smile before kissing her gently on the lips. Then he released her—and Amber felt an acute sense of disappointment. Her chagrin went deeper when he turned and walked away, back the way he had come.

Her warm passionate body felt rejected and the hurt went deeper than anything before. She was tempted to run after him, to say, 'Hamed, what is the matter, why are you going? I really do love you and I don't care that you don't love me. It doesn't matter.' But without losing what little pride she had left how could she? If Hamed had wanted her he would not have gone. He had shown her no mercy before, so why begin now?

Once Hamed was out of sight her emotions cooled, to be replaced by a burning anger that he should once more build her up to this fever pitch only to turn his back at the precise moment when she needed him most. She there and then vowed that it would never happen again. He would not make a fool of her a third time!

Amber did not see Hamed again until he joined her for dinner. She had been a little apprehensive about this next meeting, half expecting him to make some reference to their earlier conversation, and was relieved when he scarcely spoke. There was a detached air about him that puzzled her and she was able to study him without his realising the fact.

He had changed into a formal dark suit that sat elegantly on his broad shoulders. His jaw was freshly shaven and his hair neatly combed, and just looking at him caused her pulses to quicken. She did not realise how long it was that she stared, drinking in every feature of that beloved face from the straggling brows that shadowed his magnificent dark eyes, to those generous lips that she knew could wreak havoc with her senses, she only knew that suddenly he was speaking to her and that he had repeated his question twice before she become aware of the fact.

'Perhaps I should ask what it is that fascinates you about my face instead of whether you would like to go out dancing this evening,' he said cynically. 'Have I a smut on my nose or something?—you have been gazing at me for a full five minutes.'

An exaggeration to say the least, thought Amber, but she had been guilty of staring and delicate colour suffused her cheeks that he should have observed her curiosity. 'I'm sorry,' she whispered, and trying to excuse herself, added, 'I was miles away. I wasn't really looking at you.'

'Then it's a pity,' he returned with a dry smile. 'I was flattering myself that you found my face so irresistible you could not tear your eyes away. Where were you, may I ask, that made you completely oblivious to your surroundings?'

Amber shrugged. 'My thoughts can be of no interest to you.'

'On the contrary,' said Hamed quickly, 'anything you do concerns me, but I will not press you as you are so clearly reluctant to confide. Tell me instead whether you would like to go out dancing this evening?'

Could she bear the thought of surrendering herself into his arms, of the exquisite torture of feeling his body next to hers? The answer must be no if she was to remain faithful to her vows. She was exceedingly vulnerable where this man was concerned and her only form of defence was to keep as far away from him as possible. 'I don't think so,' she said, realising he was still awaiting her reply.

Those thick mobile brows rose until they almost disappeared into the thatch of hair which had already escaped and fallen across his forehead in its customary manner. 'You surprise me. I thought you might see it as a chance to—er—give me the slip. Have you given up all idea of running away? Are you perhaps finding life here more enjoyable than you at first thought?'

What could she say? She had laid the trap herself. 'I do like it,' she admitted reluctantly. 'You have a very beautiful house.'

'That is why I want a beautiful lady to live in it,' he returned softly. 'You are like a breath of spring. I wish——' He stopped abruptly, a mask falling over his face which had softened in the dimly lit room. Now harsh shadows appeared, almost as though he regretted his sentimentality. 'Then we will go for a walk,' he said, and it was a command, not an invitation.

As soon as their meal was finished Amber fetched a coat to protect her against the chill evening air which quickly followed the warm autumn days. As they let themselves out of the house Hamed took her elbow to guide her down the stone steps and out through the covered arches to the poolside. A whisper of breeze

stirred the palm fronds, their feathery outline clearly
visible against the bright night sky, and the olives
shivered as they passed through their shadowy rows.

It seemed to Amber that they walked for miles before
the trees finally thinned and then she caught her
breath in surprise. They were practically on the shore.
The sound that she had thought was a deepening sigh
of the trees was the surf as it ebbed gently across the
pale sand. An almost full moon looked as though it was
spilling silver tears across the dark depths of the
Mediterranean and it was all so very beautiful that
Amber could not help exclaiming out aloud.

Hamed smiled indulgently. 'An evening for
romance, if one were so inclined.' It was the first time
he had spoken since they set out and Amber wondered whether he had regretted his decision. But now
he draped his arm about her shoulders and led her forward on to the beach.

She tensed beneath his touch and shrugging herself
free ran on ahead, not wishing the intimacy such a
scene suggested. But Hamed's long legs soon closed
the gap between them and his fingers bit into the soft
flesh of her arm, spinning her about. 'Does my touch
suddenly repel you?' he asked harshly.

In the light of the moon his face appeared pale—
and taut—and his narrowed eyes compelled her to look
at him, to stare into that handsome face which had
become so dear to her. Mutely she shook her head.

'Then why are you running away? Are you afraid?'

'Of you?' asked Amber weakly. 'Of course not,'
knowing full well that her answer should be yes, she
was afraid—afraid of the feelings he invoked, afraid
of the way her pride deserted her at his touch when

she wanted nothing more than to be gathered into his arms and feel his strength flowing into her.

'Little liar,' he said thickly. 'Do you think I don't know what's on your mind? You want me as much as I want you, but you're scared to give yourself away. My timid little English rose does not want to become involved, so she is denying her love. Do you think that by so doing I will change my mind about marrying you?'

What answer could she give? How could she say, 'Do you love me, and if you do then everything is all right, I will marry you'? It was not a question one asked a man. If he loved her then surely he would tell her. It all came back to the same thing: he had to have some other motive for bringing her here. Love did not enter into it. She was a fool to have allowed herself to become involved in the first place. 'You're like all men,' she said scornfully. 'You only pursue what you can't get. Once you've achieved your objective it's all over.'

He shook her then, saying harshly, 'Do not compare me with my English counterpart. If I ask a girl to marry me then I am sincere. If we made love it would make no difference. I should merely be taking what would ultimately be mine by rights.'

'And how many other girls have you said this to?' Amber wanted to ask, but without giving away Rafika how could she? Instead she satisfied herself by saying, 'The difference in my case being that you haven't *asked* me to marry you.'

'Because I knew damn well you'd say no,' he rasped, his fingers unrelenting on her arm, his face thrust aggressively forward. 'Forgive me for saying so, my dearest Amber, but in this instance I know you better than you know yourself.'

The nerve of the man! Amber struggled to escape, but to no avail, his grip only tightened, but his anger appeared to have evaporated, for he was laughing now, a mocking laugh that incensed her even further. 'So you *know* I want to marry you. How interesting! Pray, tell me what else you know about me that I don't know myself?'

Her sarcasm was not lost on him, but neither did it appear to anger him as she had hoped it might. 'I know all sorts of interesting facts. Perhaps I'll tell you one day, when the time is right.'

'And what's the matter with now?' asked Amber furiously. 'I object to you talking to me in this way.'

'Then lower your defences. You might have a pleasant surprise.'

'And you just might take advantage.'

'I doubt you'd ever let me do that. Perhaps I was wrong when I likened you to a rose, you're more like a prickly pear.'

'Good,' snapped Amber, 'then perhaps you won't bother to touch me.'

'It could be worth the trouble,' he mocked. 'The fruit inside is delicious.'

'Oh, why do we bother to talk? We always end up arguing.'

'Only because you obstinately believe I have some ulterior motive,' he said, releasing her now and staring out across the sea where the moon cast its magical path.

'Have I any reason to think differently?' she asked, rubbing her arms where his fingers had held her, aware of the pain but even more alert to the pain round her heart. Was falling in love always like this? If only she knew! If only there was some way of knowing what went on inside Hamed's mind. If only Rafika had not added to her doubts. If—a little word with a wealth of meaning.

'You could try trusting me,' he said, swinging round so that the moon was behind him and his face in shadow so that she could see no more than his outline.

She wanted to trust him, desperately, but how could she when she knew otherwise? 'It's not as easy as that. You're different from me, can't you see that, Hamed? Your culture is different from mine. It would never work out.'

'I disagree.' She could tell from his voice that he was frowning, that her words had upset rather than hurt him. 'I am only half Arab, the other half is as English as you.'

She knew this, but even so it did not alter the fact that their lives were poles apart. His outlook on life was much broader than her own. She believed in being true to one man, whereas Hamed had had a succession of girl-friends, each receiving his share of devotion and given to understand that they were the only one for him. This was what mattered most, and it was something that Amber could not easily forget, nor forgive. 'Really, Hamed, you have an answer for everything! I see no point in continuing this conversation. It can get us nowhere.' She turned and headed back towards the long rows of olives, which flourished more near to the shore owing to their partiality to sea breezes.

Their leafy branches dappled the moonlight into intricate patterns across the colourless sand. Amber walked swiftly, her head down, blind to where she was going, expecting Hamed to come after her and hurt and surprised when he did not.

She reached the house and her room without seeing anyone and sank down on to the bed, not realising until then that her limbs were shaking. Each meeting with Hamed left her feeling spent, and she wished there was some way in which she could avoid these clashes. It would not be so bad if she knew where she stood, but her position was so hazy. Hamed wanted to marry her, but he had still not said he loved her; desired her, yes, but that was a very different matter and not one that Amber particularly cared to think about.

The room felt stuffy and she pushed open her windows, stepping out on to the balcony which overlooked the front of the house. The long winding road leading to the main highway stretched out before her. It was tempting to say the least, but she knew that the walk would be a long one, several miles in fact, and it was doubtful she would get far before she was missed. Besides, she did not really want to go—it was only at times like this when she felt the need to get away, when Hamed had angered her so much that her love was pushed into second place.

A step behind her caused her to swing round and she frowned when she saw Hamed standing there. 'How dare you enter my room without knocking! Is there no privacy in this place?'

'I did knock, my dearest heart, but you did not hear, so I took the liberty of entering. Are you admiring our Tunisian landscape by moonlight?'

Ignoring his question Amber said, 'If you've come

here to continue our argument you're wasting your time. There's nothing further I wish to say to you.' It was cold, but without pushing past him Amber could not get back into the room, and at this particular moment she had no desire for further physical contact between them. It was the surest way to lose a battle.

'I came to tell you to be ready early in the morning. We are going out.'

She could see him waiting for her reaction, his eyes guarded, clearly expecting her to refuse. 'Is that an order?' she asked coolly. 'Would it make any difference if I said I didn't want to go anywhere with you?'

'Not at all,' he replied. 'I want you to see some more of the country which is to be your home. I suggest you pack a few clothes as we shall be staying overnight.'

Under different circumstances Amber would have been overjoyed at this prospect, but now she felt nothing but suspicion. Their last trip, when they had gone to Tunis, had ended up with him bringing her here. How did she know that he had not made other more devious plans?

'You look alarmed,' he continued. 'There is no reason. You will come to no harm, but you will catch cold standing out here without a coat.' He stepped back into the room and Amber followed, unable to control the shivers which ran through her body. Hamed strode to the wardrobe and pulled out a thick woollen cardigan which he thrust into her hands. 'Next time you go out there at night,' he said tersely, 'wrap yourself up. I don't want an invalid on my hands. Be ready at seven sharp.'

He went then, leaving Amber looking after him in bewilderment. He had not made it sound like a pleasure trip and he had not looked as though he would enjoy it either. Why then bother to take her out? Oh, she wished she understood him! His moods were so contradictory that she never knew where she stood from one meeting to the next.

Lying in bed later she wished she had asked him where they were going. Once she had had time to think about his suggestion she quite looked forward to the trip, not that she would let him know. She intended being as unco-operative as possible if only to teach him that she objected to being bossed about in this manner. An outing planned between the two of them would have been perfect, but his high-handed manner did nothing but arouse her defences.

At six the next morning Fatima woke her with her breakfast on a tray. 'Orders,' she explained simply when Amber looked at her in surprise. 'I am asked to tell you not to be late.'

Amber pushed herself up and settled the tray safely on her lap. 'Did Hamed say where we were going?' she asked, pouring herself a cup of coffee which looked good and strong and hot.

Fatima shook her head. 'Nothing except that you were starting early. Shall I pack your overnight case?'

'If you wouldn't mind.' Amber bit into a warm flaky roll which she had spread liberally with butter and very sparingly with fig jam. 'Tell me, Fatima, does your master often take days off? I understood from Rafika that he was a very busy man, yet he seems to me to have plenty of spare time.'

White teeth gleamed as Fatima smiled knowingly. 'For you, miss, the master can always find time, but soon, when the olives are ripe, then you will scarcely see him.' She held up a white towelling bikini with a matching jacket. 'I wonder whether you ought to take this?'

Amber was as wise as the young Arab girl. 'If I knew where we were going I could tell you.'

'You do not know either?' Fatima looked puzzled for a few moments before she broke into another of her wide smiles. 'Ah, I see, it is to be a surprise. Then I will pack it so that you will be prepared for anything.'

I certainly need to be that, thought Amber. She never knew quite where she stood with this arrogant man who had disrupted her life so completely.

It was not surprising that as she washed and dressed a knot of apprehension tightened her throat and unsettled her stomach and by seven o'clock she was feeling decidedly nervous. What was in store for her? What surprises did the day hold?

CHAPTER NINE

PROMPTLY at the appointed hour Amber went downstairs. As she expected Hamed was ready and waiting, and she could not prevent a quickening of her pulses. He wore a long-sleeved knitted shirt in palest cream and cotton slacks in only a slightly darker shade hugged his hips and muscled thighs. In contrast his skin looked darker than ever before and his glowing eyes pierced her own with an intensity that made her heart skip a beat.

'Good morning,' he said, coolly eyeing her loose-fitting cotton dress of mint green. 'Why aren't you wearing something I bought for you? Why revert back to your own? Do you not approve of my choice?'

'Your choice is excellent,' admitted Amber, 'but I feel more at ease in this. I don't feel so much like a—a kept woman.'

Her choice of phrase displeased him. His eyes narrowed and a pulse beat visibly in his jaw, but he refrained from commenting, merely saying, 'Let's go. My car is ready.'

The first few miles were covered in silence, the powerful Mercedes effortlessly eating up the distance, hardly feeling the bumps in the dirt track. Out on the main highway they headed south and Amber could not resist asking where they were going, even though she had vowed to herself to show no interest at all in this outing.

'Our first stop is El Djem to see the Roman amphitheatre. It is a sight you must not miss, and is second
only in size to the Colosseum in Rome.'

This appealed tremendously to Amber, but she refused to give Hamed the satisfaction of knowing it,
merely saying politely, 'And then?'

The heavy brows rose in their characteristic way.
'We will leave that as a surprise. Don't you like surprises, my pretty friend?'

Amber flashed him an angry glance. His calm, almost
insolent tones filling her with rage. 'Not if it's like
the one the other day. That was supposed to be an
innocent day trip to Tunis, and look where I ended
up!'

He cast her an oblique glance. 'I am sorry you are
still not happy. Perhaps after these next two days,
when you see more of what my country has to offer,
you will change your mind.'

'I doubt it,' retorted Amber shortly.

'As I have said before,' he said impatiently, 'you
sometimes do not know your own mind. I have spent
many years in England and I agree it is a beautiful
country, but it cannot compare with Tunisia. Only
here will you find true happiness that comes from
beauty and simplicity, plus the refinements I can offer
you. In time you will learn to love this country as
deeply as I do myself.'

It was easy for him to talk, thought Amber, this was
his home—he had not been brought here against his
will. He did not crave freedom, to be able to do what
he wanted instead of being told. For how long would
he order her about like this? Would it be the same
when they were married?—*if*, she corrected herself

quickly, angry for having accepted the situation. Was he the type of man who was never happy unless he was giving the orders? What sort of a life would it be? It was not her nature to be subservient. Sometimes it was nice to have someone make a decision for her, but not to the extent which Hamed went. This she could never accept and if he did not change life would be eternal conflict.

'I'm not disputing the fact that Tunisia is everything you say it is,' she said at length, 'but surely even you must see that there's a difference between being forced to live somewhere and being there of your own free will.'

'But you will change your way of thinking,' he said with a curious shrug of his shoulders, 'once you have got rid of your animosity.'

'My animosity is directed at you, not your country,' she flung back. 'You and your ruthless determination to get what you want regardless of consequences!'

He smiled, still unperturbed. 'When one meets a woman as beautiful and desirable as you, but who is equally determined not to be won, one has to be ruthless. Gentle persuasion would get me nowhere, my dear Amber.'

'I am not your dear Amber!' Her golden eyes flashed and two spots of high colour burned in her cheeks. 'Nor am I likely to be if you continue treating me like a—like a child who's not old enough to make up her own mind.'

'You are nineteen. Many people in my country are married with children by this age. I do not look upon you as a child nor, I hope, do I treat you as one. All that is wrong with you is that you are unsure of yourself. It is perfectly natural under the circumstances, but given time you will adapt.'

'Ah,' pounced Amber, 'so you do realise what you're doing to me. Perhaps I should be grateful for that!'

The eucalyptus trees lining the road flashed by on either side of them and they passed through villages, the low, flat-roofed white houses hiding the inner courtyards, the minarets of the mosques stretching up towards the sky, but Amber saw none of this. As on her last ride with Hamed the man himself took up all her attention. His easy talk and condescending manner caused her mind to spin in a turmoil. What could have been a pleasant day was again being turned into an unnerving experience.

'I suggest you forget a little of your aggression,' he said calmly, but with a determined firmness to his jaw. 'You could be pleasantly surprised. I certainly do not intend to spend two days with you in this mood. I planned this trip thinking it would give you pleasure and I do not intend that you throw it back in my face.'

Amber sniffed. 'And if I don't change, what then? Do we go back, or do you think up some other form of torment?'

His knuckles gleamed white on the wheel—the only sign that he was angry. 'I could drop you off on the side of the road. There are plenty of virile young men who would be eager to take you into their homes. You know from experience what your peaches and cream complexion does to them.'

'The same, no doubt, as it does to you. You're no better than they are—the only difference being that with your money you can afford to go a different way about it.'

At that precise moment a dog, followed by a small dirty boy, chose to run across the road in front of them. Hamed jumped on his brakes, shouting a mouthful of Arabic as he did so. When the boy sat down in the middle of the road cuddling the puppy and apparently oblivious that he had almost got run over, Hamed wrenched open his door and climbed out, unceremoniously picking up the boy, together with the dog, and dumping them down beside the wall of a house. He stood there for a few moments admonishing the child and Amber saw this as a time to escape. She already had her fingers on the handle when she saw the youths on the other side of the road. They must have been standing there all the time, openly admiring her. She knew, without even Hamed's warning, that she would be followed if she so much as attempted to walk down the street.

But she could not help looking across at the boys when Hamed got back into the car and seeing what had attracted her attention he said tersely, 'You are free to go, if that is what you want.'

God, she'd rather have a thousand Hameds than one of those leering youths, but she would not admit this. 'I'll stay here,' she said stiffly, but could not resist adding, 'Better the devil you know than the devil you don't know.'

Conversation between them dwindled after that and Amber tried to concentrate on the surrounding countryside. Between the townships which appeared like oases with their scattering of palms the land was often barren. Miles and miles of plain with only an occasional shrub struggling for survival—and sometimes great ugly ravines.

Just as she was beginning to wonder when the journey would end Amber saw in the distance a giant shadow which as they drove nearer was transformed into the amphitheatre standing high above the town which surrounded it. She sat up, instantly alert, her face brightening for the first time that day.

Hamed parked the car and together they wandered around the ruin, ignoring the locals who offered to be their guide, and the young girl who begged for, 'lipstick for momma', or 'mascara', touching her eyelashes in a very feminine way for one so young.

'A lot of the locals have taken stone from here for their homes,' explained Hamed, his hand protectively on her arm. For once it felt warm and comforting and Amber had no desire to pull away. 'But you can see how impressive it used to be. Those three tiers of arcades used to seat thirty thousand people. Can you imagine them all cheering and shouting while some poor Christian prisoner was pulled to pieces by the lions?'

Amber shuddered, picturing the scene only too vividly in her mind. 'I don't know how they could watch such a horrible thing. I know I couldn't.'

'I agree, but there is a story of a certain young man named Alipuis who was induced to come here much against his will. He was determined to keep his eyes shut while the fighting went on, but the shouts and screams were too much for him and he looked. Although it was horrifying he was so fascinated that from that moment on he could not drag his eyes away and he found himself shouting and cheering with the rest of them. He became addicted after that and although he did not want to go he could not help himself and apparently admitted that he enjoyed watching humans struggling for their life against the lions and that the warm smell of blood was intoxicating.'

Amber screwed up her face in horror. 'How awful! How could he? It's barbaric!'

'It was sport to them,' shrugged Hamed. 'Have you seen enough?'

She nodded and although the ancient building now held no trace of its former savagery—the sunbaked bricks a lovely warm honey colour and birds flying happily through arches and nesting in the galleries— she could not push from her mind the scene conjured up by Hamed's story.

He kept his arm about her shoulder until they reached the car, and somehow Amber did not mind. Those few moments in the empty theatre had helped build up a rapport between them which she felt it would be a pity to break if they were to be confined so closely together during the next forty-eight hours.

Soon they were approaching what Hamed fondly termed 'The Sea of Olives'. For miles they drove through olive groves with the trees stretching out in every direction. 'There are eight million of them,' he explained, 'and for the villagers in this region it is their livelihood. If they have a good crop they are rich and can invest in more trees, or perhaps marry and pay the dowry in trees, but if there is a drought and the trees do not fruit then they are destitute.'

'Is there no other way in which they can make a living?' asked Amber. 'It seems a bit hard if they have to rely entirely on the weather.'

'So does any farmer,' he said, 'but they do also make

soaps and lubricants from the crushed stones, and the wood of old trees which have become barren is used for carving, or making looms, or for fuel.'

Amber noticed that he still did not volunteer any information about his own olive business and wondered why he was so reticent about himself. Judging by his house and standards it was a very successful business with none of the worries of drought bothering him.

They drove for nearly another hour before Hamed stopped again. This time in Sfax, the second largest city in Tunisia, where they drank coffee and took a leisurely look around the shops.

Soon they were on their way once more and the tension between them had gone completely. Amber found him a charming companion as he chatted about the various aspects of Tunisian life and commented on any passing scenery that he thought might be of interest.

It was close on lunchtime when he slowed down the car. 'How would you like lunch at an oasis?'

Amber nodded happily, immediately picturing them sitting beneath the shade of a few palms in the desert, a picnic lunch spread about their feet. The fact that they were driving between hundreds of date palms did not occur to her until Hamed stopped the car in front of a hotel. He laughed at her wide-eyed surprise. 'This is Gabes,' he said, 'one of the largest oases. It has over three hundred thousand palms and twelve great saucers of water. After lunch we will walk through it. The experience is something you must not miss.'

But before their walk they spent some time on the beach which backed on to the hotel. Replete from their lunch, they enjoyed relaxing on the warm white sand, and the sun here was much hotter than further north. With Hamed in this convivial mood Amber felt she could go on like this for ever and later did not need much persuading to go for a swim. The sand and the palms, the sea and the sun, were like a drug, intoxicating her senses, until she was chatting and laughing with Hamed as though she had not a care in the world.

Later, walking through the labyrinth of footpaths through the oasis, they held hands, Amber exclaiming in delight at the palms laden with almost ripe dates, the olives and figs, the pomegranates and flowers. It was like a fairytale place and she was glad she was here with Hamed. They walked across narrow palm tree-trunk bridges spanning little streams and here and there were fences made from palm fronds laced together, and a thousand different scents filled the air.

Near one of the pools beautiful yellow flowers grew and strange-looking butterflies hovered. The final climb brought them out on the cliffs where, looking back, the valley floor was breathtakingly beautiful with its palms and fruit trees mirrored in pools with rushes growing near their banks.

Amber listened with interest when Hamed told her that just as the people living near the olive groves relied on the olive for their livelihood, so too did the oasis dwellers rely on the palms. 'They crush the stones into ersatz coffee or fodder,' he said, 'they use the fronds to thatch roofs and make furniture, the trunks to build footbridges and roofs, and the fibre to weave into rope.'

He pulled a low-growing stalk off one of the palms

and plucking a shiny brown date popped it into
Amber's mouth. It was delicious and her eyes were as
shiny as the fruit themselves when she asked for another.

Her childlike enjoyment amused him and he played
a game popping the dates into her mouth. 'Of course,'
he continued, 'although the oasis dwellers more or less
live off the palm they also give it a large part of their
working life. They need to bore wells to water them,
and they prune them meticulously. And then there
is the mating.'

This last statement made Amber laugh. 'Mating?'

'Yes. Did you not know that the palm is unisexual?
In June every year the men climb all the male palms
and get pollen from their flowers which they then put
on the female flowers to ensure pollination.'

This information was news to Amber, but of course
this country had opened up a whole new way of life to
her and made her realise that all the comforts she had
taken so much for granted at home in England meant
nothing to the people out here. Yet they were happy.
Not once had she seen a Tunisian who had not had a
pleasant smile. Despite their poverty they seemed content and she guessed that this meant more to them than
having cars and stereograms and automatic washers.

Back at the car she felt almost too awed to speak
and their journey continued in silence. This time,
however, it was a companionable silence and she felt
happier than she had since first meeting Hamed. They
were driving across plains now, with only occasional
eucalyptus trees and soon not even them. The sun
shining through the windows had a soporific effect on
Amber and soon she was asleep, unaware of Hamed's

tender glances or that his hand stroked her shiny, sun-kissed hair.

She did not wake until the car stopped, then looked apologetically up at her companion. He smiled indulgently, his devastating good looks once more sending her senses into a whirl. 'I—I'm sorry,' she stuttered, 'I didn't mean to be so rude.'

'You did not miss much,' he said, 'and riding a long way is always tiring.'

It occurred to her that Hamed himself must be tired. All the time she had been asleep he had driven, needing to keep fully alert. She glanced at her watch, noting with amazement that it was after six. 'Is this where we're staying?' she asked, looking out at a rosy brick wall with an entrance in brown, blue and beige Italian-type tiles.

He nodded and together they climbed out of the car, stretching their stiff limbs, glad to be free from the confined space. They walked into the reception room where Hamed spoke in rapid Arabic to the man behind the desk. Amber wandered through another door opposite which led outside into a huge sandy area where white chalets with thatched roofs stood in neat orderly rows. A central area was set out with gaily coloured tables and chairs and behind that a larger hut which, when she looked through the doorway, turned out to be a dining room. Palms waved their feathery fronds above—and dusk was gathering. It was yet another fairytale place in this whole new world Hamed was showing her.

When Hamed appeared she followed him willingly between the rows of huts. He stopped in front of a painted brown door and inserted a key into its lock,

swinging open the door before standing back to allow
Amber to enter.

Inside it took a few seconds for her eyes to adjust
to the gloom, for the only window was tightly shut-
tered. It was not until Hamed came in too, putting
down their cases and closing the door behind him
before snapping on the electric light, that the full
import of what was happening struck her. There were
two beds in the room and a small table and a mirror.
Nothing else. But what registered most were the beds
—two of them! She looked from them to Hameḍ and
back again. 'Does this mean that—you——'

'I'm afraid so,' he said, his voice apologetic but his
face showing not the least concern.

'I might have known there would be some catch in
it!' Amber's voice rose as she glared at the dark man
leaning back indolently against the door, his thumbs
hooked into his belt. 'I suppose you planned this all
along—soft-soaping me so that I would raise no objec-
tions. Well, you're wrong! You either find yourself
another room or take me back right now. I refuse to
sleep in here with you!'

He sighed. 'Much as I regret the situation there is
nothing I can do about it. We were lucky to get this
room. It's not often they're full up. I've never had to
book before, but it appears they had an unexpected
coach party and this is the only hut left.'

'I don't believe you,' declared Amber flatly. 'I saw
no one. The place looks deserted.'

He shrugged helplessly. 'Go and ask for yourself.'

'Don't worry, I intend to,' she retorted, wrestling
with the door handle and pulling on the door so that
Hamed was forced to move.

But the man behind reception spoke no English, only Arabic and French, which was just as bad. Amber's knowledge was limited to what she had learned at school—which was not very much since she had not had much interest. Now she wished she had as she furiously tried to tell the man what she wanted, using sign language and speaking in very slow, very clear English. 'I—want—another—room.' When Hamed appeared she rounded on him hotly. 'I bet you planned this as well! How much have you given him to pretend he doesn't know what I'm talking about?'

'Do you really believe I would do such a thing?' asked Hamed, frowning tightly. 'Believe me, I have no wish either to spend the night alone with you.'

'You can't really expect me to believe that!' snapped Amber, aware that the other man was watching them with interest, his elbows leaning on the desk, his bright eyes swivelling from one to the other. He was waiting now for Hamed's response, confirming her suspicion that he knew what they were saying. Nothing would make her believe that this had not all been arranged and that this dark-skinned Arab was in on it too.

'It is the truth,' he returned simply. 'I have no desire to spend the night in the room of a woman who is afraid.'

'If you're going to make this into a personal argument, let's get out of here,' grated Amber. 'Your friend here is *listening* to every word we say, and don't try to tell me he doesn't understand, because you won't convince me.'

Back in the small room with its two beds covered in hand-woven blankets she rounded on Hamed. 'You're so right, I am afraid. Afraid that you might take it into your head to rape me. It's what you planned all along, isn't it—you just didn't want to do anything so sordid in your own house in case the servants found out.'

Hamed's eyes narrowed until they were no more than slits. The shadows cast by the single light bulb threw the rest of his face into harsh angles and his breathing deepened until she could see his chest rising and falling.

'Do not drive me too far, my pretty one, or you might find those beautiful features marked for life.'

'And I expect you'd enjoy doing that,' she slung back, uncaring that she angered him further. 'It's just what you would like—hurting someone weaker than yourself!'

'I might at that,' he said thickly, grasping her arms and pushing her down on to one of the beds, 'if you try me far enough.'

And in his present mood Amber knew that he spoke the truth, so she said no more for the moment. She would wait until his temper had abated. Then she would again tackle him about sleeping together in this tiny room. There must be something that could be done. Surely they could discuss it like rational human beings instead of bawling at each other.

After looking down at her for a few angry seconds Hamed turned and left the room, closing the door with such violence that the light bulb swung on its wire, causing the shadows in the room to eddy about her. The walls and roof were wood-panelled, the bed-covers in dark reds and browns, and the floor concrete with a black woollen rug. It was sombre and somehow frightening. A stupid thought when just outside the door was a world full of beauty. It was her row with Hamed that had done this to her, made her afraid that something lurked in the dark corners. She brushed her hair and then went outside to find the toilet block which Hamed had pointed out earlier.

It was clean and airy and painted white, making her realise how ridiculous her fears of a few moments ago were. But it was empty, and this puzzled her. If the place was full where were all the residents. When she had washed and returned to the hut she changed into a yellow slack suit that buttoned up to the neck and had long sleeves, because although the day had been one of the hottest she had known so far the evening air was chilly.

Soon Hamed came back. The tenseness had gone out of his face, but he had lost that carefree attitude of the afternoon and Amber was sorry. He had been at his best then and if it had not been for the fact that she was expected to share this room with him everything would have still been the same. 'Are you prepared to talk this thing over rationally?' he asked.

Amber nodded, afraid to trust her own voice, for a sudden certainty that he had spoken the truth assailed her, leaving her nerves trembling.

He sat down on the second of the two beds, as far away from her as he could get. 'I would not lie to you, Amber. I have no reason to. I had planned this trip with the very best of intentions and I was as shattered as you when they told me that these were the only two beds left.'

'But——' Amber threw her hands apart helplessly, 'where is everyone? It looks deserted.'

He smiled then, his teeth looking very white in the

dimness. 'This was to be another of my surprises. They have gone on a safari into the desert. I am afraid we shall have to wait till morning before we can make our trip.'

'Safari? On camels?' Amber knew she sounded stupid, but she needed confirmation that she had heard him aright.

He nodded. 'Only for a few hours, but it is yet another experience to add to your collection. Did you know that we are right on the edge of the Sahara?'

'No, I didn't.' She had known they had travelled a long way, but having fallen asleep had lost all track of where they were going. 'These camels—are they safe?' She was not so sure she wanted to ride on one of those huge swaying beasts.

Her apprehension made him laugh. 'You won't be left to cope alone. It's a tourist gimmick really, their owner will lead you there and back, but you certainly cannot come this far without going into the Sahara. The sand there is like none other, so fine and white it is unbelievable.'

'I see, so that's tomorrow settled, but what about tonight? What are you going to do about that?'

'What can I do?' he asked, his lips tightening fractionally.

Amber lifted her chin. 'I should have thought a man of your status would have no difficulty,' recalling Rafika's words that he was a respected man. 'Or hasn't your reputation reached this far?'

'If you want to try and walk home, that's all right,' he shrugged, 'but as for me, I'm tired, and I'm not going another step until I've had a good night's sleep.'

In all fairness Amber knew he made sense, but some

determined streak made her insist. 'So you don't care how I feel. My reputation doesn't matter. Who do you think is going to believe that we slept in the same chalet but that it was all perfectly platonic?'

'No one's going to know unless you tell them,' he insisted harshly, brutally. 'You're really being very silly over this whole thing and I don't want to hear another word. You'll be perfectly safe with me. I'm too damn tired to care whether you're in the same room or not. You could be another man for all the notice I'll take of you.'

What else could she say? He had made it perfectly clear that he no longer found her desirable and although it was a relief to know that no attempts would be made on her virginity it hurt that he should so coolly and calmly reject her.

Suddenly they heard noise and voices outside. The others had returned. Hamed stood up and opening his canvas bag took out a towel. 'I'll freshen myself up before dinner. Why don't you take a look around?'

There wasn't much to see. The rows of chalets were all the same, except that somehow they looked different now that crowds of holidaymakers were milling about. They were a mixed crowd, French, German, Dutch—Amber heard all sorts of languages.

Behind the chalets were tents where the staff slept. They were made from a thick woollen material in shades of natural to dark brown, draped over wooden poles. Hand-woven bedding was spread out on piles of brushwood near the entrance to these tents. The camp looked deserted and Amber, driven by curiosity, peeped inside one of the tents. It was scrupulously clean, but contained nothing except a few brightly woven rugs and some orange boxes. Presumably they used these tents for sleeping in only, their meals being taken at the hotel.

A few minutes later Hamed joined her. He had changed into a pair of blue jeans topped with a thick navy sweater. 'Ready for dinner?' he grinned, as though nothing had happened. 'I'm starving!'

Realising it would be juvenile to carry on their argument Amber smiled and nodded. The meal was superb. They started with tomato salad, followed by *briks* which, Hamed told her, were a close rival to the *couscous* for the national dish. The *brik* consisted of a triangle of super-light pastry folded round an egg and deep-fried. 'You eat it like this,' he smiled, as Amber doubtfully eyed the delicacy. He picked up a corner in each hand and bit boldly into the centre, taking care that the egg did not run down his chin.

Amber was more conservative, nibbling her way along the edge until she reached the egg, but she had to admit that the *brik* was delicious. The main course consisted of chunks of meat in gravy together with potatoes, peas and carrots, followed by a dish of pomegranate in syrup. Amber found this fruit entirely delicious and wondered how long it had taken for them to pick all those seeds from the fruit or whether it was done by machine.

They sat for a while over their coffee before moving outside where many of the other residents had now gathered. The crowd were in high spirts. The bar was open and they sipped their drinks beneath the stars. When one of the Germans started a sing-song they all joined in and later some of the local waiters made up an impromptu band with their *zoukra* pipes and a *tabel* drum. One of the French girls rose and gave a fair imitation of a belly dancer, gyrating her hips with more suggestiveness than grace, and after that it was a free-for-all, each one getting up and doing a turn whether it was singing or dancing or even a gymnastic display. Soon Amber and Hamed were the only two who had not participated and amidst much hand-clapping they were forced to take the floor.

'I can't do anything,' hissed Amber, 'I've never been any good at this sort of thing.'

'You can dance,' he said, 'we will dance together, then perhaps you will not feel embarrassed.' So to the mournful wail of the *zoukra* and the rhythmic beat of the drum he pulled her into his arms, holding her body suggestively close and pulling her head down on to his shoulder. Amber closed her eyes and with the feel of his hard body next to hers she could almost forget that they were being watched. She and Hamed were sharing this romantic evening beneath the tropical night sky where only the stars winked down and the palms whispered between themselves.

When he began to sing it caught her by surprise and she stopped. They stood like that in the middle of the arena, Hamed holding her at arm's length, his smiling face looking down into her upturned one. She had no idea what he was singing, since he used his native tongue, but it sounded like a love song and judging by the rapt expressions on their audience it was having an equally moving effect on them. When his song finally finished they returned to their seats. The crowd cheered and clapped, but Amber was only aware of the magnetism that drew them together. It had been so very strong during those few minutes on the floor.

It was a pity that the evening had to end, but one by one the crowd drifted away until at length Hamed stood up. 'Are you ready?' he asked.

Ready for what? she thought, attempting to stifle the sudden rapid beating of her heart. Ready for sleep —or was there something else he had in mind despite his earlier assurance?

'In a few more moments,' she said shakily. 'It's so peaceful here under the stars, I wish it could go on for ever.'

He smiled, plucking her hand from her lap and pulling her to her feet. 'Nothing lasts for ever, my little romantic, nothing.'

But she knew that her love would. No matter what he did or how he treated her. It was something much bigger than herself.

CHAPTER TEN

BACK in their little square room Amber could not still her quickened pulses and felt sure Hamed must be aware of her unease. Not that he himself seemed perturbed. He whistled softly to himself as he pulled off his sweater, but when he began to unzip his jeans Amber hastly turned her back, pretending to be searching in her bag for a comb. It was not until he said, 'Come along, slowcoach,' that she turned.

He wore only a pair of black silk pyjama trousers and Amber's consternation was so great that it threatened to choke her. Was he going to stand and watch her undress? Hadn't he the decency to turn his back as she had done? 'I thought you were tired,' she said, hoping he would take the hint and climb into bed. But he merely smiled and perched himself on the edge.

'Our relaxing evening has revived me. I don't feel in the least like sleep now.'

Amber toyed nervously with the buttons on her jacket, realising that she couldn't stand there for ever in the hope that he would do the decent thing. She was quite convinced that he was deliberately watching and that he was enjoying her discomfiture. 'I'm sure if you tried you would have no difficulty,' she said.

'Something tells me you are trying to get rid of me,' he said, still with that aggravating smile. He rose and came round the bottom of the bed towards her. 'Dearest Amber, why are you terrified of me? Didn't I give you my word?'

She licked suddenly dry lips, praying he would not touch her. She knew that if he did she would not have the power to resist. Those hours spent beneath the stars had triggered off a primeval reaction and she ached for his touch, while at the same time her pride would make her fight with all her strength if he so much as attempted to. She had no intention of breaking her vow never to give in to him again. 'I—I'm not afraid,' she said. 'What makes you think that? Your word is good enough for me.'

He came a step nearer, so close that she could feel the warmth emanating from his body. 'Then why are you trembling, my little passion flower? Look, your fingers are shaking so much you cannot undo your jacket. Allow me,' and without giving her the chance to refuse he unfastened the buttons. She was uncertain whether it was an accident that his hand brushed her breast, but it made her catch her lip between her teeth and she was sure that he must hear the wild beating of her heart.

'Thank you,' she whispered, when he would have slipped the jacket from her shoulders. 'I—I can manage now,' adding beneath her breath, 'Oh, please go to bed! Don't you know what you're doing to me?'

He tipped his head to one side and stood back a pace, grinning sardonically. 'If you need any more help just say the word. I'm more than willing to oblige.'

'I bet you are,' she flung back, her breathing easier now that he had moved slightly away. 'You're an expert at this sort of thing, aren't you?'

'You could say that,' he acknowledged easily. 'Most

women seem to get confused with me watching. I wonder why?'

She could have told him. She could have said that his smouldering dark eyes did things to a woman that should never be allowed, that one glance from beneath those thick dark lashes turned a woman's limbs to jelly. But she didn't. Instead she said, 'You're conceited. It has nothing to do with you watching. It's merely a matter of pride. Maybe I'm old-fashioned, but there are occasions when I like privacy and this happens to be one of them.'

'Are you ashamed of your body that you don't want your future husband to see it?' he mocked, still refusing to move.

'As a matter of fact,' Amber was feeling desperate now, 'I don't believe you really intend to marry me—not that I shall ever agree,' she hastened to add, 'but I think you—you're only trying to get out of me what you can. Perhaps I ought to tell you now that you're wasting your time. I'm not one of those girls who hop into bed with any man who cares to ask her and then forgets all about it afterwards. I'm a one-man girl and whoever I marry I shall have to be darn certain he loves me first.'

He nodded his head solemnly. 'Admirable sentiments and I agree wholeheartedly. But you fail to mention your own feelings. Would you need to love this lucky man just as much, or wouldn't that matter so long as he loved you?'

'Of course I would love him. Marriage can't be one-sided.'

'And what sort of a man are you looking for to fulfil these worthy conditions?'

His open mockery whipped up her anger. 'Certainly not anyone like you!' she flared. 'I want a man who will treat me with respect.'

'You mean you want a weak little yes-man who would do everything you say and vow his undying love?' His face mirrored disgust.

'Don't be ridiculous,' she snapped. 'You know what I mean.'

'I know what you want,' he said tightly, 'and it isn't what you think. You need someone who will set fire to your blood, someone to make you feel all woman so that you make love as wildly as you are now arguing.' He paused, his face brooding, his eyes dark and unfathomable. 'In other words,' his hands were on her shoulders now, 'you need me,' and he pulled her to him so that she could feel the throb of his desire.

She felt herself drowning in the tide of her emotions, but even so knew that she must resist. To give in now would set the seal on her future. Her arms were pinned to her sides, but she still had on her shoes—and his feet were bare! Without stopping to consider the consequences she ground her heel on the top of his foot, feeling a sadistic delight when he yelled out and let her go.

'Perhaps now you'll realise that I meant it when I said you were not my type,' she said, smiling a little, but not altogether sure what his reaction was going to be. Looking down at his foot she saw that the high heel of her sandal had drawn blood and she immediately regretted her action. She had not meant to hurt him—not that much. When she looked back up at his face his expression frightened her. It was menacing but sexually exciting at the same time, and her pulses began their erratic race all over again.

'You deserve punishing for that,' he said thickly. 'I know I promised not to touch you and I'm not normally a man who goes back on his word, but I'll make you pay if it's the last thing I do.'

Amber cast a scared glance towards the door, but the key was missing. There was no escape that way. 'I—I'm sorry,' she began, 'I—I didn't——'

'Sorry be damned,' he broke in. 'You knew what you were doing, but it's a pity it's had the opposite effect to what you hoped.'

Her jacket had swung open in the affray, revealing the curves of her breasts. His eyes dropped to them now and with a harsh exclamation he ripped the coat from her shoulders, dropping it to the floor. Her bra followed and he did not stop until he had her stripped naked. Her attempts to check him were ineffectual and when he had finished she stood, her eyes downcast, all fight gone out of her, knowing without a shadow of doubt what he was going to do next and equally sure that nothing she could do or say would halt him.

But strangely enough it was her very meekness that had the desired result. Now that the aggression had gone out of her Hamed too appeared to lose interest. 'For goodness' sake put your nightdress on and get into bed,' he said tersely.

She needed no second bidding and within seconds was lying between the white cotton sheets, crying silent tears for Hamed—because he desired her, but did not love her.

For what semed like hours she lay still and silent—and awake, listening to the creak of the other bed as Hamed tossed and turned. Was he troubled too or was it merely the strangeness of their surroundings that kept him awake?

When she could bear the loneliness no longer she called out softly, 'Hamed, are you awake?'

A long pause before he said, 'Yes, it's too warm. I'm going to open the shutters. I would have done it before, but I thought I might disturb you.'

She sat up and looked at the luminous hands on her watch—just after three and she felt wide awake. She hoped Hamed would sit and talk, but he got back into bed and this time fell into an immediate sleep. She could hear his breathing, deep and rhythmic—and envied him.

A breath of wind came through the mosquito mesh —it was welcome and the last thought Amber had before she too fell asleep was that she would like to see the sun rise over the Sahara, hand in hand with the man she loved.

She dreamt they did. She dreamt that out there in the milky white desert he made love to her—and it was beautiful, like nothing else she had ever experienced. But afterwards, when he had wrung a confession of love from her, he had laughed, just as he had on that other occasion—a ruthless, calculated laugh that told her it had all been a game, and he had won.

'I hate you, Hamed,' she cried, 'I hate you!'

She had woken then, the cry of anguish still on her lips. Immediately she looked across at the other bed. It was empty, so too was the room, and she breathed a sigh of relief that he had not heard. For he would certainly have wanted to know what had brought about such an emphatic denial.

A glance at her watch revealed that it was well after

eight. So much for her early rise. She dressed quickly and let herself out of the room. The key was back in the lock! After a quick wash she brushed her teeth and then back in their hut packed her clothes into her overnight case. Hamed had already seen to his case which stood beside the door ready for their departure. He must have worked very silently, she thought—or had she been deeply asleep, dreaming about him? The memory brought a delicate flush to her cheeks and a sparkle to her eyes, and it was at this moment Hamed returned.

He studied her silently for a few seconds, but apart from saying, 'Breakfast's ready,' he kept his thoughts to himself.

'Are we still going on our camel ride?' she asked conversationally, trying to break the silence that had settled between them as they ate their rolls and sipped hot coffee.

'If you want to.' He sounded indifferent.

'Well—if you do.'

'Oh, for God's sake don't be a little martyr! Either you do or you don't and that's all there is to it. I couldn't care less myself.'

If this was going to be his attitude then neither did she—except that she had been looking forward to it. Once she had become used to the idea it had appealed to her. Besides, she might not have another opportunity. The way things were going it would not be long before she was heading back to England. 'I would like to,' she said finally with a tentative smile.

'Right.' There was no softening of his expression and she began to doubt the wisdom of this camel-trek, but she refused to change her mind now and give him something else to grumble about.

In the end she was glad she went. There were several others who had booked camels that morning and Amber found her excitement mounting as she donned a loose-fitting cotton robe, similar in style to a kaftan, and wrapped a white silken scarf about her face and hair until she could hardly recognise herself. But when she looked at Hamed her heart seemed to stop beating. This was the real Hamed. He looked the true part of an Arab—the English part of him disappeared altogether. This was his country, his way of life—and she could expect no part of it.

The brown eyes that looked at her from between the folds of white silk were deep and disturbing, probing right into her and baring her soul. She turned away to hide her confusion and walked with the others out of the hotel grounds to where the camels waited.

It was with trepidation that she climbed on to the back of the one nearest to her, helped by the smiling owner, and she scarcely heard Hamed call, 'Hold tight!' before the great beast started to rise. She just managed to grab the wooden part of the harness in front of her to stop herself from falling backwards, before she lurched forwards, finally ending up several feet in the air with a look of wide-eyed astonishment on her face.

'I meant to warn you,' called Hamed from his position on an even larger camel at her side. He was openly laughing and she wondered whether he would have found it even more hilarious if she had fallen off altogether.

'Thanks,' she returned primly. 'I'll know better next time.'

When everyone was astride their ungainly-looking beasts they set off. Amber found the swinging, ambling gait of her mount distinctly uncomfortable and clung on for dear life until after a few hundred yards she got used to the rhythm and was able to relax.

Hamed on the other hand looked perfectly at home as though he had spent his entire life riding through the desert—and of course he had no one leading him! Amber was glad though of the man who led her camel, checking him when he attempted to wander away from the others, and she was even more relieved that she was not the American lady whose camel decided to trot and she was bouncing up and down on his back in a manner that looked as though it shook every bone in her body.

Hamed had been right about the desert. Never before had Amber seen sand so white and fine. Miles upon miles, broken only by occasional scrub or palms, bewitching, awe-inspiring, casting a spell over her as had no other part of Tunisia. Exactly why she did not know. Whether it was the vastness or the fact that it opened up a whole new concept on life, she was not sure, but whatever it was she felt at peace with herself and those around her. Hamed's indifference was a thing of the past and she smiled up at him. 'I think I'm beginning to enjoy it.'

Perhaps he too felt the change of atmosphere, for he did not ignore her. He nodded, 'I thought you might,' and as a curious groan came from her camel, causing her to look at the animal in alarm, he said, 'Do you know why the camel holds his head so disdainfully?'

Thinking it some kind of joke Amber laughed and shook her head.

'Because, according to their Arab masters, although man knows the ninety-nine names of Allah the camel knows the hundredth.'

Now she knew he was teasing and she was glad he had got over his moodiness. She had not been looking forward to their journey home, not if he continued with the silence that had begun at breakfast.

A few miles into the Sahara they stopped. This time Amber was ready when her camel lowered himself to his knees in his peculiar three-stage manner. They climbed a sand dune and sat in the shade of the palms, and she loved every minute. Hamed was close, as close as he could be without their bodies touching. He was gazing at the horizon and there was nothing on his face to say what he was thinking.

'Haven't camels got ridiculously long eyelashes?' said Amber, more for something to say than because it was particularly interesting. Hamed in this mood left her slightly puzzled and unsure exactly where she stood.

'They are to keep out the sand,' he explained, turning then and squinting at her through the sunlight which was full on his face. Faint lines appeared round his eyes and tiny specks of sand glistened on his eyebrows. His lips were parted slightly and she wanted to kiss them, to bring to life the dream that he had made love to her out here in the desert. She wanted all these other people to go away and leave just the two of them alone. 'When there's a sandstorm,' he continued, unaware of the line her thoughts were taking, 'he falls to his knees and stretches his neck along the sand, closing his eyes and nostrils. His master shelters behind him, wrapping himself completely in his burnous.'

The moment had gone. Amber felt disappointed. 'I wanted to get up early this morning and see the sunrise,' she said.

'You would have been unsuccessful. I had the same thought myself, but it was too cloudy. In fact I walked out here hoping the clouds would shift.'

That must have been when she was dreaming about him. If he had invited her to go with him it could have come true. There were no clouds about now. The sky was a true clear blue, the sand warm beneath their fingers, but all too soon it was time to go.

Hamed helped her to her feet and held her hand as they slithered down the sand dune, but once they were on level ground he let it go and climbed up on to his camel without bothering to see that she was all right herself.

On the homeward trek he was once again morose and silent and this time Amber made no attempt to draw him into conversation. There seemed little point when he so clearly did not want to be bothered. It hurt, for her love grew with every hour that passed, until the thought of parting from him was as painful as though he was a living part of her.

Back at the hotel they collected their cases and set off on the long trip back. In Gabes Hamed branched off to their right and Amber knew that this was not the way they had come. 'Where are we going?' she asked, her voice sounding curiously stifled in the stillness of the car.

'To Matmata—you have heard of it?'

Amber had, and had in fact intended taking a trip there from the Sahara Beach to see these troglodytes who lived in holes in the ground. She had been fascinated when she first heard of them and excitement caused her now to say, 'The pit people? Oh, lovely, I didn't realise we were so near.'

Hamed smiled at her exuberance, for a brief space forgetting his ill-humour. 'You are perhaps beginning to realise that my country is a land of contrasts. You have seen the olive groves and the oases, the cities and the desert, and now you are about to see this strange lunar-like landscape where people have lived in underground dwellings for over two thousand years.'

'I heard that the authorities have tried to persuade them to move into more conventional type houses?'

Hamed nodded. 'It is true, but they prefer their way of life, and who can blame them? Their homes protect them both against scorching summer days and freezing winter nights. They are as comfortable as you and I and probably happier.'

Amber agreed on this last score, knowing that unless by some miracle Hamed returned her love she would never again realise true happiness.

They drove along a smooth straight road passing a seventh-century shrine of Sidi Boulbaba, Barber to the Prophet Mohammed, and a small would-be museum which Hamed told her had been awaiting inauguration for at least ten years. They passed some barracks and two wartime bunkers and a small settlement of white *logements*, before rising into the Mountains of Matmata.

Here were peaks and domes as well as eroded gulches, and in almost every hollow was a few palms and a dwelling. The path rose steeply, twisting and turning through the rose-coloured mountains until suddenly they rounded a bend to find a view of the Matmata Valley.

It was a scene Amber would not forget in a hurry. The broad expanse of sand was covered with crater-like pits, while above, white mosques and new homes somewhat marred the effect.

Hamed parked the car, brushing away the touts who instantly came to try and sell their souvenirs. He seemed to know where he was going and Amber followed as he strode towards an archway cut into the side of the hill. They went through this tunnel-like entrance and she found herself in a courtyard about twenty-five feet in both diameter and height. The blue sky was their roof—and even a few leafy trees grew there.

A well-built woman of indeterminate age came forward, smiling broadly and shaking Hamed's hand—obviously she knew him very well. They spoke in Arabic, but Amber's attention was taken up by the woman herself, not their conversation. She was dressed in a gorgeous red *mellia*, a sari-type garment wound round the waist and held over the bust with two silver pins that caught the end below her shoulders like dungaree braces. Her blouse was white and lacy, and over her hair, which was dyed bright orange, was tied a purple silk scarf. Her face was lined and her eyes a surprising blue.

'Bournaouia says we are quite welcome to look around her home,' said Hamed, taking Amber's hand and leading her forward.

The trees in the courtyard had surprised Amber, but the rooms that led off were even more astonishing. In the bedroom the beds were scooped out of alcoves in

the wall, and in the kitchen was a stove with provisions
piled neatly either against the wall or on shelves dug
out of the walls themselves.

'I wonder why they chose to live like this in the
first place,' she said, completely spellbound by the
comfort and cleanliness of it all. She had expected
nothing like this. Inside it was like a real home. The
walls were whitewashed, and there were handmade
rugs on the floor. It was cosy and comfortable, everything you could ask for.

'Some historians say that the Berbers built them to
escape their enemies,' replied Hamed, 'but a more
likely explanation is that the stone is too soft to build
with, so they dug into it and as you can see the result
is surprising. Their homes are more sophisticated than
some of the people living on top. The women work
hard, though, very often having to walk seven or eight
kilometres for food.'

A knotted rope helped the pit-dwellers up to the
next 'floor' where there were store rooms for cereals
or olives. Amber was fascinated and when she was
offered a cup of tea she had no thought of refusing.
The liquid was thick and black and like nothing else
she had ever tasted, but she drank it politely, and shook
hands with Bournaouia before leaving, asking Hamed
to express her thanks for allowing them to see over her
house.

There was also a troglodyte hotel, converted from
a set of pits, but Hamed allowed her no more than a
cursory glance. He seemed anxious to be on their way.
Amber had found it a very satisfying experience and
said as much to Hamed as they drove back to Gabes
for their lunch.

'Has your opinion of Tunisia now changed?' he asked, 'or are you still against making it your home?'

Amber had grown to love the country and its people and knew that even if she did not stay here now she would return one day for another holiday. But what to say in response to Hamed's question? She could not say, 'I would love to live here and marry you, but only if you say you love me. If you don't there's no point.' At least she still had sufficient pride to avoid the humiliation such a statement would cause. She could imagine Hamed, those deep brown eyes crinkling at the corners with laugher that held no humour, his lips turning up at the corners, but not smiling. He would say, 'Why is love so important to you, my passion flower? Is it not enough that I have found you sufficiently attractive to ask you to marry me?' He would never admit that he loved her—for the very simple reason that he did not. She doubted him capable of ever truly loving anyone. He enjoyed playing at love but without ever totally committing himself. When she realised he was still waiting for her answer, she said, 'I loved your country from the first moment I set foot in it, but my home is England. I could never truly belong here.'

He frowned. 'I do not think you are being fair to yourself. You are all the time fighting the tide of emotions that threaten to take over. Would it be so bad, loving me? Why don't you let yourself go and give yourself a chance to see that I am not the ogre you make out?'

'And then let you cast me aside when you've satisfied your—your lust?'

Hamed's lips thinned. 'You still insist on believing Rafika.'

'What other proof have I?' snapped Amber. 'Besides, right from the beginning I knew what you were after. And when you failed, when your outsize male ego had a shock, you thought up another way to make me your bed companion. I wonder, would you really go through with a wedding ceremony just to satisfy your perverted little mind?' As soon as the words were out she wished she could retract them. She hadn't meant to say that, but he infuriated her, always insisting that she was afraid to reveal her true feelings. The more so because he was right!

For a few long seconds there was silence, a dreadful silence, a silence so tangible that Amber felt that as soon as either of them spoke it would shatter into a myriad tiny pieces. All that could be heard was Hamed's deepened breathing. He was angry, rightly so, and fighting for control. She waited with bated breath for her retribution which must surely come. He would never let her get away with that.

'You think I wouldn't?' he ground out slowly. 'You think that even I would never have the nerve to go that far?'

He trod on the brakes and pulled into the side of the road. Then he turned towards her, reaching out to twist her head towards him, his fingers digging painfully into her jaw. The stormy depth of his eyes held a threat that made her tremble beneath his touch. 'How well do you know me, my passionate little friend? How well?' He shook her until her teeth rattled. 'Not well enough, I'm afraid. Our wedding has already been arranged. Four days from now you will be my wife, and there is nothing you can do about it.'

Amber stared at him in horror, unable to believe that she had heard correctly. 'You're a beast!' she cried at last, desperately pounding her fists against his chest. 'You're odious and I despise you!'

His voice became dangerously calm. 'Then it will be my pleasure to teach you to love me.'

'Never, never in a thousand years—and let go of my face, you're hurting!'

'I want to hurt you,' he rasped, 'as your words hurt me. I want to beat you until you are begging for mercy.'

'Then why don't you?' she flung back. 'Go on—I may as well find out now what type of a—*husband* you're going to be—a taste of what the future holds in store,' and before she could control them tears raced down her face—tears of anger against this barbaric man, and tears of sorrow for the love he had just killed.

CHAPTER ELEVEN

AMBER thought the tension had been bad between them before, but it was even worse now. Hamed drove the Mercedes fast and furiously, not even stopping for lunch, passing through Gabes without a thought that his passenger might be hungry. Not that she was. The thought of food choked her, but the least he could have done was ask.

She sat back, her eyes closed, her hands gripping the edge of her seat as though fearing for her life. But it was not Hamed's driving that bothered her, it was her own present unbearable situation. She had had no idea that Hamed had actually set a date for the wedding. It had been a tremendous shock, and now her mind whirled round in circles trying to see some way out. She had never really thought he was serious, believing that as soon as he tired of her he would let her return to England. Now she knew differently, and her only way out of the situation was to run away.

There was no way that she was going to marry a man who had hit her! She raised tentative fingers to her cheek. It still burned from the imprint of Hamed's hand. She had taunted him, but it was not until she felt his hand against her cheek that she had believed he would carry out his threat. She refused to consider that it might have been to stop her hysterical outburst.

After that Hamed had started up the car again and since then he had not spoken. Her tears of anger had turned into tears of self-pity until finally they stopped altogether. She was aware that her face must look a sight, but Hamed had put her handbag in the trunk together with their cases, so there was no way of repairing the ravages of her tears.

Their journey back would take several hours, for she knew it must be at least three hundred kilometres. It would probably be dark. Perhaps as well, since she could go straight to bed. After a day spent with Hamed in this intolerable atmosphere it would be a welcome relief to be alone.

From beneath her lowered lashes she stole a glance at the man at her side. He drove the car with grim determination, his hands firmly on the wheel, his face set in stern lines. Amber doubted he was even aware of her regard. He had shut himself away in a world where she had no part. She wondered how long this would last, whether he would perhaps keep it up until their proposed wedding day. If she was still here! With a bit of luck she would be back in England.

What would be the best way to escape? she wondered. It was very rarely she was left alone, as she had already discovered; her only chance would be at night when everyone was asleep. Even then it would be difficult. The road from the house to the main highway was several miles of dirt track—she would never manage that carrying two heavy suitcases. Even if she left her clothes behind she would still have a long way to walk. Hamed's house was situated roughly halfway between Sousse and Tunis, she knew that much, but exactly where she had no clear idea, and the little villages they passed through were not exactly the type of places she could go for help.

Perhaps she ought to risk telephoning for a taxi, but even so, without the address she would feel an idiot. She wished now that she had kept his business card instead of tearing it up in temper.

One other route open to her would be to take Hamed's car—if she could find out where he kept his keys—then, once he was asleep, she could make her getaway in style. This latter idea seemed the most favourable, and satisfied that she had now sorted things out Amber settled back into her seat, her eyes closed once again.

She dozed spasmodically for most of the journey, tired after her restless night, but not wishing to sleep deeply, thus leaving herself in a very vulnerable position. Hamed's mood frightened her. Oh, very often he had been displeased, but never as coldly furious as he was now.

They stopped once, a very short stop in Sfax, but he did not ask if she was hungry, seemingly oblivious to the fact that they had eaten nothing but a couple of rolls early that morning.

Amber was relieved when they at last turned off the main road on the last stage of their journey. When he pulled up outside the house she watched carefully to see what he did with the keys, delighted to see that after opening the trunk he put them back into the ignition. It looked as though it was all going to be easy.

The heavy studded door opened as they approached, little Mohammed beaming at his master and relieving him of their cases, trotting upstairs with them without having to be told.

Amber made to follow. She was stiff and tired and looked forward to a soothing bath to wash away the grime of these memorable two days.

'Just a minute.' Hamed's voice grated into the empty hall.

Amber turned slowly, glaring defensively into the solemn brown eyes that looked at her coldly.

'If you are thinking of trying to run away I should forget it. Dinner will be served in one hour. Please make sure you are here.'

She tightened her lips and swung away without bothering to answer. How had he known? By what uncanny method had he read her thoughts? But she would not give him the satisfaction of knowing he was right. She would be polite enough this evening, if that was what he wanted. She would give no indication that she was in a hurry to return to her room ready to make her plans for her escape that very same night. He must never guess.

The Slouma household ran on smoothly oiled wheels. By the time Amber reached her room Fatima was already unpacking and had the bath running.

'You had a good time?' she nodded, as though it was a foregone conclusion. 'But I expect you are glad to be home.'

Home! The girl spoke as though she was already married to Hamed. But Amber smiled agreeably, realising it would not be wise to arouse even Fatima's suspicion that things were not all they should be.

It was bliss to soak in the scented water, to just lie there and let all her cares and worries float away, and she realised with a twinge almost approaching sadness that she would miss all this. These last few days had been a taste of heaven. She had tasted life as it might have been married to Hamed, living in a sun-kissed land with all the luxuries his wealth could afford.

She still loved him, despite what had happened this morning. She knew that now. She would probably love him for the rest of her days. It was not a thing that could be shrugged to one side because something went wrong. It was a coveted part of her, to be kept in a secret place and only looked at when she was alone.

At that point Fatima knocked discreetly on the door and called, 'You will have to hurry, miss, if you don't want to be late for dinner.'

Roused out of her daydreams, Amber towelled herself dry on one of the fluffy jade towels, wishing she had had time to wash her hair, but resigning herself to the fact that a good brushing would have to suffice.

Fatima had already put out her dress. It was one of the new ones Hamed had bought, a silky cream strapless gown that she knew would follow her curves with more than a hint of sensualism. She couldn't possibly wear that. What would he think—that she had changed her mind as he was so determined to marry her and thought she might as well make the best of it? No chance. She was searching through her wardrobe with nothing on but her briefs when she heard Fatima behind her. 'Oh, Fatima,' she said, without turning, 'I couldn't possibly wear that. Hamed doesn't like me in anything revealing.' It was the best excuse she could think of on the spur of the moment.

'On the contrary,' came the voice of the man himself, 'I like you just as you are—and what could be more revealing?'

Amber pulled a dress from the rail and held it up in front of her before spinning round to exclaim furiously. 'You don't own me—not yet—so get out of here!' She did not like the way he was looking at her, his eyes devouring her body, insolently moving over every inch. He stepped forward and ripped away the protecting dress, allowing his fingers to brush her sweet-smelling skin, lingering on the smooth creaminess of her breasts.

'I shall enjoy possessing you,' he whispered harshly, his hand moving abruptly up to her hair and pulling back her head so that to move would cause pain. His lips parted hers in a ruthless savage kiss—punishing her, yet at the same time igniting the passion she so desperately strove to deny.

When he had satisfied himself he threw her from him so that she fell across the bed, on top of the dress that Fatima had so carefully laid out. 'I'll give you two minutes to get downstairs,' he said, 'and that dress will do admirably. It was for just such an intimate occasion as the two of us dining together that I chose it.'

Again Amber felt near to tears. She could see what he was trying to do. Each day now, if she remained, she would have to put up with these humiliating scenes until the final moment when she would irrevocably belong to him. That would be his biggest moment of triumph—when he could claim her body and she would be unable to do a thing about it.

The dress, as she had guessed, was perfect if she wanted to play the part of a temptress, but under the present circumstances she felt nothing but embarrassment. Nevertheless she held her head high as she entered the dining room, trying to ignore the colour flaming in her cheeks. Her only consolation was in the thought that tonight she would run away. It had to be tonight; she could stand no more of these undignified scenes. This thought, and this thought alone, gave her the strength to get through the evening.

Despite their tiring day and his marathon drive Hamed gave no sign of weariness. Indeed he kept Amber talking until well after midnight, almost as though he knew what she was planning. This did not surprise her. He had an uncanny way of reading her thoughts and although she tried to keep her attention on the conversation her eyes were frequently drawn to her wrist watch, a fact that did not go unobserved by her companion.

When eventually he decided it was time for bed he walked upstairs beside her, kissing her long and completely outside her bedroom door. 'Goodnight,' he said pleasantly, waiting for her to go inside. A few moments later she knew what it was all about. A tiny click on the outside of her door made her frown and turn the handle. It refused to open. 'Hey,' she called, 'what is this? What have you done?'

'A small bolt—just in case you should get any ideas,' came the smooth reply. 'Pleasant dreams, my passion flower.'

Pleasant dreams indeed! Amber kicked the door angrily, forgetting for the moment that she had open-toed sandals and hopping about the room a second later nursing her injured foot.

As soon as she had calmed down to think rationally, she smiled. Hamed thought he was so clever, but he had forgotten the balcony—she hoped. Tentatively she tried the door. It swung open as normal and she stepped outside. It was quite a drop, but she might just about manage it, if she was careful. He must have thought she would be afraid to try and escape this way. For the moment though she must pretend to be preparing for bed.

It had been her initial plan to make sure Hamed was asleep before carrying out her attempted escape. She would not be able to do that now, but if she gave him an hour that should be enough. It was the longest hour she had ever spent, but she dared not go sooner in case she was heard.

At half past one she stepped out on to the balcony and lowered her suitcase on an improvised rope from one of the sheets. She giggled to herself. It was like something out of a movie. Next, with two sheets tied together and fastened round the wrought iron she climbed over the railing and inch by inch eased her way down to the terrace. From here it was simple. Down the curved stone steps and—she stopped. The car had gone. This was something she had not counted on. But of course it would be in the garage. Mustapha or Rached had put it away. She ran round the house, stumbling in her haste and then almost crying in fury. The garage doors were locked. She leaned weakly back against them, fighting tears of rage, and wondering why she had not had the sense to check up on this aspect before.

There was nothing for it now but to walk. It would take longer than she had planned and she might not reach the Sahara Beach before daybreak, but she had to carry on now.

Her feet were sore and aching at the end of the first mile and her suitcase got heavier with every step. She had packed no more than a few clothes, enough to last her until she got home, but she knew she could not turn up at the hotel without a case. It would look very peculiar. And this was the only place she knew. There were hotels in Sousse, but at the Sahara Beach she had her friends, they would help.

It took her nearly two hours to reach the main highway, her progress hampered by the rutted track, and if it had been any longer she doubted whether she would have made it. The stones had penetrated through her thin-soled shoes and she had blisters on her heels, and the suitcase felt as though it was filled with lead. But at least she had managed this far. She put down her case and sat on it, oblivious to the cold night air. It was bliss to relax.

After a few minutes she made herself get up. She reckoned it had to be at least twenty miles to the Sahara Beach, but with any luck she would see a taxi or a bus before she had gone too far. In another hour or so it would be light—her chances of getting a lift then would be much higher.

There were no lights along the road, and no footpath, but the night was clear and there was sufficient light from the moon to see where she was going. Day broke in a haze of red and gold, but Amber was too tired to appreciate it, trudging mechanically along, making herself walk, knowing that if she stopped she would never get going again. Was it worth it? she asked herself time and time again. Wouldn't it have been better to go through with the whole affair? She loved Hamed, even if he did not love her. Would it be sufficient? But her answer had to be no. Marriage could never be one-sided.

When a horn blared and a car pulled up at her side

she turned in relief. It was a taxi—a dusty white Simca —with a driver who looked at her in open admiration. At any other time she would have refused to climb in, not really feeling that she could trust the fellow, but now, footsore and weary, she did not hesitate.

In no time at all they were at the Sahara Beach. She paid him cheerfully, although it seemed to her an extortionate sum, and almost ran inside the building. It was like coming home again after a long absence and she could hardly believe that it had only been four days since she was last here.

She ignored the curious looks bestowed in her direction, waiting impatiently at the reception desk until someone appeared. The bad news was like a blow. They had no vacancies. Every room was full. 'But I was here a few days ago,' she insisted, 'surely you've still got my room?' But no, it had been taken and there was no chance of another one becoming vacant. They were heavily booked for the whole winter through.

Amber turned away, her shoulders drooping, despair in every line of her body. Would it be worth trying the airport to see whether she could get her flight altered? She was supposed to be going home in two more days anyway and had hoped to spend this time here with her friends. On the other hand, it could be for the best. If she got a flight today there would be no chance then of Hamed finding her, for wouldn't the Sahara Beach be the first place he would look? She had not thought of this before. It had been the only place she knew where there was someone with whom she could talk.

A few minutes later she was through to the airport, but again her hopes were dashed. They had a flight

tomorrow but not today. Would that be any good to
her? She said it would, but the problem still remained what she was going to do with herself until
then.

She sat down on one of the deep low chairs in the
large reception area, watching the holidaymakers
walking to and fro, each intent on doing whatever it
was they had planned, each with their own circle of
friends. Only Amber was alone—tired, weary and half
afraid.

Hoping that Nicolette would pass her way she remained there for one hour, maybe two, she did not
know. She seemed to be losing all sense of time. A
hand urgently shaking her arm aroused Amber from
sleep. She opened her eyes wide with alarm, at once
thinking that it was Hamed come to take her back, and
relieved to find that it was Nicolette.

'Amber, what are you doing here? You look fright-
ful. What has happened?'

'I've run away,' she said simply.

'From your handsome Arab friend?'

Amber nodded.

'But why? We were given to understand that you
had agreed to marry him. We thought it rather sudden—but falling in love is like that, isn't it?'

'I suppose so.' Amber felt too exhausted to answer
all these questions. She just wanted somewhere to rest.
She looked round. The man behind the desk had disappeared. 'Do you think I could come up to your
room?' she asked Nicolette. 'I haven't slept all night
and I'm absolutely worn out. My old room's been
taken and they have no more vacancies.'

'But of course. We will put a "Do not disturb"

notice on and you can sleep all day. No one will know. Are you hungry? Shall I bring you some breakfast back?'

Amber shook her head. 'I'm not hungry, just tired.'

It was absolute bliss to wriggle between the sheets and close her eyes and within seconds she was asleep. Until late afternoon she slept and when she awoke for a few seconds she felt happy. Until she remembered, then it all came flooding back. Her flight from Hamed's house—the long, painful walk. She wondered what his reaction had been when he found her missing. Whether he was searching for her now or whether he had decided she was not worth the trouble. He could be here in this very hotel. She ought to have warned Nicolette not to say anything. All she could do was hope the other girl would have the sense to keep her presence here a secret. She had been too tired to tell Nicolette the real reason for running away, intending to tell her later when she had had a rest, not realising that she would sleep for so long.

She climbed out of bed and washed and changed and was sitting before the dressing table brushing her hair when Nicolette entered. 'Ah, you look much better,' exclaimed the French girl. 'I was very worried about you.'

'I'm fully recovered now,' smiled Amber, 'except for my poor feet. Have you any plasters I can put on these blisters, then perhaps I can put my shoes on?'

Nicolette had brought up some sandwiches wrapped in a serviette and Amber ate ravenously. It had been almost twenty-four hours since she last had any food and she was starving. Once she had eaten she began to talk, telling Nicolette about the way Hamed had virtually abducted her and then declared he intended marrying her. 'I didn't believe him at first,' she said, 'but now I know it's the truth. In four—no, three days' time I'm due to become Mrs Hamed Ben Slouma. He won't take no for an answer. What else could I do but run away?'

Nicolette shrugged and spread her hands in a typical Gallic gesture. 'But I thought you loved him— and he you?'

Amber looked sad. 'I do love him—but—he doesn't love me. He's just making use of me. And I couldn't stand that—that's why I must get away. I've managed to change my flight to tomorrow, but I need somewhere to stay tonight. Do you think we could get away with me staying here?'

'Why not?' said Nicolette easily. 'I'll smuggle you some more food up. No one will know.'

'And Nicolette,' said Amber urgently, 'if Hamed should come looking for me, don't give me away?'

'I think you've got him wrong.' Nicolette shook her head sadly. 'I'm sure he's not that type of man, but your secret's safe with me.'

'Thanks a lot,' smiled Amber, knowing how difficult it was for the French girl to understand how she felt, for hadn't Nicolette had a crush on Hamed herself? Would she not think it incredible that anyone should want to get out of marrying such a gorgeous man?

Nicolette spent the evening with Amber and they shared the bed, laughing a lot trying to push each other out. Amber felt much better now and the next morning was almost her usual self again.

Her plane was at lunchtime, so as soon as she had

eaten the rolls, once again secreted in by Nicolette, she left the hotel and caught the bus to Monastir airport. Nicolette wanted to come with her, but Amber preferred to go alone on this last leg of her journey.

Waiting about at the airport worried her and she frequently looked about for the tall distinguishable figure of Hamed, convinced he would come and really surprised that she had got this far without any sign of him.

When the announcement came over the loudspeaker requesting the passengers for the London flight to assemble in the departure lounge she began to hurry along with the rest of the crowd, wondering why she did not feel as happy as she should have done. Surely she did not regret running away? She knew without a shadow of doubt that their marriage would be doomed. For a few fleeting months maybe they would be happy, but after that, when Hamed tired of her, what then? Amber wanted happiness for the rest of her life—not a brief interlude and then heartbreak. She had done the right thing—*she had*.

Soon she was walking across the tarmac. The huge white plane was waiting—waiting to take her back to England with its green and tranquil fields—England where she had always been happy, where she would once again find happiness.

But would she?

The question rose before her eyes in big capital letters. Would she find true happiness?

She stopped dead in her tracks, oblivious that she had caused a minor pile-up behind her. She couldn't do it! She loved Hamed too much—she wanted him—on whatever terms.

Spinning round, she ran back into the building. She felt suddenly vibrantly alive—all the numbness of the last thirty-six hours had disappeared. There was an eagerness on her face as she hailed a taxi, disappearing only momentarily when she realised she could give the driver no address, but as soon as she mentioned the name Hamed Ben Slouma it was like a magic word, because the driver nodded and smiled and beckoned her to get in. It would cost a small fortune, travelling so far in a taxi, but she did not care. Speed now was the essence, before she lost the courage it would need to admit that she had made a mistake.

In a remarkably short time they left the main highway, bumping and shaking along the dirt track almost as though the driver was aware of her urgency. Amber strove eagerly for her first glimpse of the elegant white villa that would soon be her permanent home. Her heartbeats quickened alarmingly the nearer they got and when at last the house came into sight she almost lost her nerve and asked the driver to turn round. But she knew this would solve nothing and when she finally alighted, her fingers trembled as she pulled the necessary number of notes from her purse.

Then she was alone.

Slowly she walked beneath the cloistered terrace, unable to stop herself from looking up to see whether her makeshift rope was still there. It wasn't. Hamed had had it removed—but he had made no attempt to find her! Did that mean he did not care? That he had shrugged philosophically and said, 'Oh, well, it would have been an enjoyable experience but there will always be someone else.'

This last thought was too painful to bear and her

face crumpled—her new-found eagerness disappearing, leaving her a subdued drooping figure standing before the great door. Had she the nerve to go through with it?

The matter was taken out of her hands when the door swung open and Mohammed appeared. His cheerful face was the welcome she needed and her spirits revived as he stood back for her to enter. 'Oh, miss, *tafdddal*, we have all been so worried. Shall I tell——'

'Wait!' Amber put her hand on his arm. There was something she had to know first. 'Was—was—Hamed —Mr Slouma—worried? Did he try to find me?'

The boy shook his head. 'He shut himself in his study. He has been there ever since, refusing to eat or see anyone. I will tell him you're here.'

'No, let me surprise him.'

Mohammed nodded happily. 'That is a good idea, but I must tell Fatima. She will be so pleased.'

Amber did not bother to knock, gently pushing open the door and stepping inside. She had never been into his study before and her first impression was of dark heavy furniture—an oppressive room—but her eyes were drawn inexorably to the figure sitting at the desk, his head bowed in his hands. He looked a beaten man and although Amber was not entirely sure that she herself was the reason compassion welled up inside her, as well as her own overpowering love. As her feet flew across the floor she asked herself how she could ever have thought she could live without him. How she could have doubted her love.

Only when she touched his arm did he look up— and the pain in his eyes was such that a sob broke in her throat. 'Oh, Hamed, Hamed,' she cried, flinging her arms round his neck, 'I'm sorry!'

'For what?' he asked blankly, pulling away from her embrace as though it embarrassed him, and rising to stand by the window, gazing out across the distant fields of olives.

His rejection disconcerted Amber and for a fleeting second she wondered whether she had been wrong to come back. But then the true reason reasserted itself and she knew she must confess. Now was no time for false pride. If he still rejected her, after her admission, then that would be that—at least she would know in her own heart that she had tried. She would be able to live with herself without constantly wondering if they might have made a go of marriage if only she had told him she loved him.

So she followed him across the room, standing close behind so that she could feel his warmth. 'Hamed,' she whispered, 'I couldn't do it. I—I love you too much. I know you don't love me.' Once she had started she could not stop, the words came tumbling out. 'But it doesn't matter. I don't care any more. I just want to belong—to feel your arms about me—to—to share your bed. Oh, Hamed, I'll marry you, I will, I will,' and then, bitterly ashamed, she turned away. It had had no effect. Hamed's rigid back was still turned even after her impassioned outburst. Her vision blurred with tears as she groped for the door. The quicker she made her exit the better. She had made a fool of herself—a complete and utter fool. Whatever had possessed her to think she could appeal to this man? He cared for no one but himself, least of all her.

'Amber, wait!' His voice reached her as she lifted her hand to open the door.

She paused but did not turn. What he had to say could be said to her back. Whatever it was it would be sure to hurt.

'Come here.'

This time there was no note of authority in his voice. It was a plea which she could not dismiss. Slowly she swung about. He was looking at her now and there was a new light in his eyes. He held out his hands and she walked towards him unable to look away.

'Do you really love me?' he asked in a hushed voice.

She nodded. 'Completely—enough for the two of us —if—if you still want to marry me, that is?'

He nodded. 'Of course I do, but I don't want you to have any doubts. I don't want you to do anything you'll regret later.'

She could not swear to this, not knowing how deep his own feelings went. If, an unbearable thought, he later rejected her for someone else, she'd regret it then. She would wish she had never allowed her heart to rule her head. She said, 'That's a strange thing to say, coming from you, I thought you always took what you wanted, regardless of consequences.'

'Not if I love that person very dearly. Perhaps my methods were a trifle unusual—but you are an un-usual girl,' and he pulled her into his arms, lowering his head and kissing her very thoroughly and satisfac-torily.

When he had finished Amber pushed him away, still trying to work out whether she had heard him correctly. 'Did—did you say—you loved me?' she en-quired breathlessly.

Hamed nodded, smiling.

'But why didn't you tell me—it would have saved all this heartache.'

'I thought you'd guessed, but I couldn't put it into so many words, not until I was sure of you. Even now I can't believe it's true,' and he pulled her close again as though he never wanted to let her go.

But Amber pulled back. 'I'm still a bit frightened—about our future. Rafika said that you had promised to marry her—that it had been agreed between your two families. What are you going to do about that?'

'Rafika's still a child, cherishing childhood dreams,' he laughed. 'It's all nonsense, a story she makes up to frighten away any girl in whom she thinks I am becoming too interested. Like the china she broke. She knows I can't stand clumsiness and did that to try and get rid of you. I'm sorry I shouted—I didn't find out until afterwards what had really happened.'

Amber was glad he no longer blamed her. 'And Rafika herself, she means nothing to you?'

'I love her—like a sister, my little jealous one—not like a woman—not like I love you.' His voice deepened and he pulled her roughly towards him, kissing her with such an intensity that it was almost frightening. 'I don't think I can wait to make an honest woman out of you,' he muttered, swinging her into his arms and crossing towards the door.

Amber wanted him just as much as he needed her, but she knew that a few more days now would make no difference. 'No, Hamed,' she laughed, kicking her legs. 'I'm old-fashioned in that respect, as you well know. Besides, we've got a whole lot of talking to do. There are many things that still puzzle me.'

He laughed and set her down. 'Go ahead, ask what

you like. From now on I intend to be perfectly open with you—and you with me,' he added threateningly. 'No more trying to hide your feelings.'

'What I want to know,' said Amber, sitting on a chair near his desk, crossing her ankles daintily and looking beguilingly up at her lover, 'is how you knew who I was. That very first day in the medina you knew my name—and after that—the things you said—you knew so much. I thought you had some ulterior motive.'

'And how do you know I still haven't?' he asked, leaning back lazily against the edge of his desk, his hands thrust into the pockets of his trousers.

'Because I love you,' she said, 'and I wouldn't love a man who was up to no good.'

'Such trust—I hope I warrant it,' he mocked.

'You do,' she returned fervently. 'But come on, answer my question.'

He shrugged and looked slightly abashed. 'You're not going to believe this,' he said, 'you'll probably laugh, but it's true all the same. I fell in love with your photograph.'

This really did astound Amber. 'I don't understand. What photo? Where?'

'The one your Doctor Greer keeps in his wallet.'

'Doctor Greer? What has he got to do with it?' The more she heard the more astonished she became.

'I was taken ill while on business in England and I went to see him. I gather he was a very great friend of your family?'

'That's right, he brought me into the world, used to treat me as his own daughter. He never had children himself. But what has he got to do with it? How did he come to show you a picture of me?'

Hamed's eyes glinted. 'I asked him if he knew any pretty English girls who would be willing to marry me.'

Amber's mouth fell open in shocked disbelief and he laughed. 'No, seriously, when he discovered that I came from Tunisia he mentioned that he had a young friend who was holidaying here. Without me saying any more he produced your photograph. He is very proud of you, Amber. He told me how you had nursed your mother through her long illness and that he had had the devil of a job persuading you to take a holiday.' He frowned. 'I think he took a liking to me too, because he asked me if I would look you up and make sure you were happy and recovering from your own near breakdown.'

'And of course you jumped at the chance?' Amber felt bemused. The coincidence was unbelievable.

'I had already fallen in love with you,' he said. 'As soon as I saw your tawny eyes looking out at me from that photograph I knew you were the girl for me. There and then I made up my mind that I would marry you.'

'And go to any lengths to do it?' she asked, mocking him as he had mocked her.

'Not at first,' he laughed. 'I intended doing the whole thing properly, but when it became clear I was getting nowhere I decided to kidnap you, hoping you would find my charm irresistible.'

'What did you think when I said I hated you? Was it a blow to your plans?'

'I knew you didn't mean it,' he said. 'Your body betrayed you every time, my passionate one. Remember that night when you told me you loved me and said you didn't mind me making love to you—and I walked out?' She nodded. 'It was all part of a plan. My sadistic streak, I suppose. I thought if I played it cool the fires within you would do the trick and that soon you would come crawling. But it backfired— miserably. I couldn't keep away from you for long. That's why I took you on that trip—it was the only way I could think to keep you close without you actually guessing my motives.' He pushed himself away from the desk. 'That too was a dismal failure. You left me in no doubt then of your feelings towards me. I'm sorry if I hurt you,' he touched her face gently, 'but when I found out that everything I had done was in vain I couldn't help myself. I was in a blind fury. I think I could have killed you.'

'But you didn't.' Amber took his hand and kissed it, holding it against her cheek. 'You came up fighting, declaring that you were still going to marry me no matter what. That's what frightened me. I loved you desperately, but I didn't want to marry a man who didn't return my feelings, or who had no compunction about hitting a woman.'

'Please,' his face mirrored pain. 'Don't remind me about that. I can't apologise enough. It won't happen again, I assure you. But what I can't understand is why you came back, after all that. Weren't you afraid, knowing how violent I could become?'

'I was willing to risk it,' said Amber softly. 'I'd made up my mind that a few months' happiness would be better than a whole lifetime's misery.'

She lifted her face to his and his kiss was infinitely sweet.

'One last thing,' she said, when he eventually let her go. 'Would you really have let me return to England? Despite this great love you say you have for me would you have let me go without making any effort to stop me?'

Hamed shook his head. 'I was having one great fight with my pride. I wanted to come after you, you don't know how much, but I had hurt you enough trying to keep you here. I couldn't inflict any more hurt. But I would have come—eventually. When we had both had time to know what it was we really wanted.'

'I'm glad it never came to that,' said Amber. 'I don't think I could have lasted out. Please, Hamed, hold me tight. Never let me go again.'

'I won't, my dearest,' he whispered harshly. 'I won't. We belong to each other now—for all time.'